D1264478

STUDIES IN COMPARATIVE ECONOMICS 3

Studies in Comparative Economics

1. E. H. Phelps Brown, THE ECONOMICS OF LABOR
2. Charles P. Kindleberger, FOREIGN TRADE AND THE NATIONAL ECONOMY
3. Theodore W. Schultz, TRANSFORMING TRADITIONAL AGRICULTURE

TRANSFORMING TRADITIONAL AGRICULTURE

by Theodore W. Schultz

NEW HAVEN AND LONDON
YALE UNIVERSITY PRESS

Second printing, January 1965.
Designed by Sally Hargrove.
Set in Baskerville type
and printed in the United States of America by
The Carl Purington Rollins Printing-Office
of the Yale University Press, New Haven, Connecticut.

Library of Congress catalog card number: 64–12661

FOREWORD

Modern economics has been bred chiefly in Western Europe and the United States, and despite its aspiration toward generality it bears the stamp of institutions and issues characteristic of these areas.

But the economic world no longer revolves about London and New York. Dozens of new nations are struggling toward economic independence and industrial growth under institutional arrangements quite unlike those of the West. Economies of a novel type also extend eastward from central Europe to the Bering Strait and have been busily developing their own principles as a by-product of administrative experience. It is asserted that "Western economics" has only limited analytical value in these other countries.

The problem of the content and relevance of economics thus arises inescapably. Are the economic principles taught in the West really susceptible of general application? Or are they culture-bound and relevant mainly to industrial capitalist countries? Is it possible to create a general economics which would be as useful in Poland or India as in Canada or France? Or must we be content with several species of economics which will remain distinct in intellectual content and applicability?

"Comparative economics" has been regarded as a separate area of the economics curriculum, consisting of a botanical classification of national economies into a few loosely labeled boxes. But surely any course in economics is potentially comparative. A concern with comparative experience can profitably be infused into any of the standard branches of economic study. This series is inspired by the hope that a rethinking of particular branches of economics in world perspective, combined with a bibliography of available material from many countries, may help teachers to give their courses a broader and more comparative orientation.

In pursuing this objective, we deliberately chose autonomy over standardization. Each author was left free to determine his own approach and method of treatment. The essays thus differ considerably in length, analytical as against descriptive emphasis, geographical coverage, and other respects. How far the original intent of the series has been accomplished is for the profession to judge.

We are grateful to the authors who have struggled with possibly insoluble problems, to the Ford Foundation for its support of the enterprise, and to the staff of the Yale University Press for their helpful cooperation.

The Inter-University Committee on Comparative Economics: Abram Bergson, Arthur R. Burns, Kermit Gordon, Richard Musgrave, William Nicholls, Lloyd Reynolds (Chairman)

PREFACE

When I see how little success most countries are having in increasing agricultural production, I can see why one might well believe that it is a rare and difficult art to master. If it is an art, a few countries are very adept at it though they seem unable to transmit this art to others. Those that are adept are increasing production while decreasing both labor and land devoted to farming. But as long as the economic basis of increasing production is thought to be an art, I do not wonder that economic policy to achieve it should be so largely in the realm of myth. Presently, in country after country, policy makers are about as sophisticated in this matter as farmers who once upon a time planted crops according to the face of the moon.

While agriculture is the oldest production activity of a settled community, surprisingly little is known about the incentives to save and invest where farmers are bound by traditional agriculture. Oddly enough, economics has retrogressed in analyzing the savings, investment, and production behavior of farmers in poor countries. The older economist had a better conception than economists now have of the particular type of economic equilibrium relevant under these circumstances.

Although it is obvious that traditional agriculture is niggardly, it is not obvious that this niggardliness is *not a function* of a unique set of preferences related to work and thrift.

Nor is it obvious that it is predominantly a consequence of farmers having exhausted the profitability of the "techniques of production" which are an integral part of the inputs and knowledge at their disposal, and that there is little or no incentive to save and invest in order to increase the stock of the forms of reproducible capital farmers are employing. The purpose of this study is to show that the crucial feature of traditional agriculture is the low rate of return to investment in agricultural factors of the type that farmers have been using for generations, and to go on to show that in order to transform this type of agriculture a more profitable set of factors will have to be developed and supplied. To develop and to supply such factors and to learn how to use them efficiently is a matter of investment—investment in both human and material capital.

Food and agriculture have served economists time and again as a testing ground for new concepts and analytical tools. Diminishing returns to labor and material capital against land and Ricardian rent are examples. So is the income elasticity of the demand beginning with Engel's statistics, followed by the monumental study of Henry Schultz and then studies by Girshick and Haavelmo, Stone, Tobin, Burk, Houthakker, Goreux, and others. Recently there has been the testing of the explanatory value of distributed lags by Nerlove, specification bias in production functions by Griliches, and research costs and social returns from a new input, hybrid corn, also by Griliches. In this study I attempt to test the usefulness of a supply and demand approach in determining the price of income streams from agricultural sources.

I intended when I started this study to include an extensive bibliography of the relevant literature. But it soon became clear to me that the available literature, although large with respect to many features of agriculture in poor countries, is in general not germane to the basic economic issues which are the core of this study. I therefore decided against a separate listing and in favor of additional footnotes for this purpose. It turns out that many of the published items to which I refer represent views and treatments that support doctrines and policy approaches which are inconsistent with my analysis.

Since I began this study late in 1959 I have incurred many obligations. I have learned much from the dialogue I had with my students when I presented the central ideas of this study to them. My colleagues, Zvi Griliches, D. Gale Johnson, and Dale W. Jorgenson, read key chapters and I benefited much from their criticism. Vernon W. Ruttan read all of an early draft, and I accepted nearly all of his suggestions. Abram Bergson, Richard A. Musgrave, and Lloyd Reynolds raised useful questions. My wife, Esther Werth Schultz, corrected manuscript, checked references, and convinced me time and again that what I had thought was clear still lacked clarity. Mrs. Marian Neal Ash of Yale University Press gave unstintingly of her editorial talents. Mrs. Virginia K. Thurner, my secretary, corrected proof with painstaking care. I also am indebted to the librarians at the University of Chicago for their help. A Ford Foundation fellowship freed me from my university duties during 1961–62. But more than any other obligation is what I owe to the oral tradition that is a part of the workshops in economics at the University of Chicago.

Theodore W. Schultz

The University of Chicago
May 1963

CONTENTS

TRANSFORMING TRADITIONAL AGRICULTURE

1 THE PROBLEM AND ITS SETTING

The man who farms as his forefathers did cannot produce much food no matter how rich the land or how hard he works. The farmer who has access to and knows how to use what science knows about soils, plants, animals, and machines can produce an abundance of food though the land be poor. Nor need he work nearly so hard and long. He can produce so much that his brothers and some of his neighbors will move to town to earn their living. Enough farm products can be produced without them. The knowledge that makes this transformation possible is a form of capital whenever it is an integral part of the material inputs farmers use and whenever it is a part of their skills and what they know.

Farming based wholly upon the kinds of factors of production that have been used by farmers for generations can be called traditional agriculture. A country dependent upon traditional agriculture is inevitably poor, and because it is poor it spends much of its income for food. But when a country develops an agricultural sector such as Denmark has in Europe, Israel in the Near East, Mexico in Latin America, and Japan in the Far East, food becomes more abundant, income rises, and less of the income of the country is spent for food. How to transform traditional agriculture, which is niggardly, into a highly productive sector of the economy is the central problem of this study.

Basically this transformation is dependent upon investing in agriculture. Thus it is an investment problem. But it is not primarily a problem of the supply of capital. It is rather a problem of determining the forms this investment must take, forms that will make it profitable to invest in agriculture. This approach treats agriculture as a source of economic growth, and the analytical task is to determine how cheaply and how much growth can be realized from transforming traditional agriculture by means of investment into a more productive sector. This problem has received only scant attention even though the study of economic growth has flourished. Economists who have been studying growth have with few exceptions put agriculture aside in order to concentrate on industry, despite the fact that every country has an agricultural sector and in low income countries it is generally the largest sector. Meanwhile, many countries are in some measure industrializing. Most of them are doing so without taking comparable measures to increase agricultural production. Some are industrializing at the expense of agriculture. Only a few countries are obtaining substantial economic growth from both industry and agriculture. It is the exceptional country that is successful in developing its agricultural sector so that it is a real source of economic growth.

But there are no basic reasons why the agricultural sector of any country cannot contribute substantially to economic growth. True, agriculture using only traditional factors cannot do it, but modernized agriculture is capable of making a large contribution. There is no longer any room for doubt whether agriculture can be a powerful engine of growth. But in acquiring such an engine it is necessary to invest in agriculture, and this is not simple because so much depends on the form the investment takes. Incentives to guide and reward farmers are a critical component. Once there are investment opportunities and efficient incentives, farmers will turn sand into gold.

The purpose of this study is to show that there is a logical economic basis why traditional agriculture employing only the factors of production at its disposal is incapable of growth except at high cost, and why the rate of return to investment in modern agricultural factors can be high by past growth standards. Thus it really does matter what is done in developing agriculture in countries that want to achieve economic growth as cheaply as possible.

At the risk of elaborating the obvious, it may still be prudent to state what is meant by the "agricultural sector." It is the sector of an economy that produces a particular class of products, products that come mainly from plants and animals, including poultry. Some of these products consist of fibers and other raw materials used by industry. But most are used ultimately for food. It will be convenient to classify the production activities of the agricultural sector as follows: (1) production by farmers (peasants and cultivators in the terminology of this study are farmers; they may produce mainly for home consumption or wholly for markets); (2) production of agricultural factors not by farmers but by suppliers from whom farmers acquire them; and (3) production entering into the marketing, transportation, and processing of agricultural products that is not performed by farmers.[1]

But why the lack of understanding of the economic potentials of agriculture? It stems partly from the state of economic knowledge and partly from confusion caused by widely held doctrines about the agricultural sector. In the realm of knowledge, agricultural economists have restricted their studies predominantly to farming in that small class of countries in which agriculture has been most successful in contributing to national income, examining all manner of problems confronting these farmers but not the economics of growth from agriculture. In general they have neglected traditional agriculture, leaving it to anthropologists, who have made some useful studies as will become evident later. Meanwhile, growth economists have been producing an abundant crop of macro-models that are, with few exceptions, neither relevant in theorizing about the growth potentials of agriculture nor useful in examining the empirical behavior of agriculture as a source of growth.

Of course economists and informed people generally are becoming aware of the large differences among countries in the rate at which the productivity of labor in agriculture has been increasing; it has been rising much more rapidly than in industry in those countries most successful in modernizing agriculture. There is also an awareness of the correspondingly large differences in rate of increase in agricultural production. But these differences have gone un-

1. Another useful way of classifying the production activities associated with agriculture has been presented by Harold Breimyer, "The Three Economies of Agriculture," *Journal of Farm Economics, 44* (August 1962).

explained. Growth economists, theorizing at a high level of generality, have with few exceptions been committed to disembodied "capital" and "labor" as the basic explanatory variables. There is then a residual which is attributed to "technological change." When these models are used to analyze real data, it turns out that most economic growth is concealed under the heading "technological change." Because it is a residual, there is no explanation for it. At the same time, those who have taken any notice whatsoever of the agricultural sector always abhor the backwardness of farm people. They conclude that the economic stagnation of traditional agriculture will be overcome when farm people learn the economic virtues of "work and thrift," and thus of saving and investing—yet never a thought is given to the profitability of investment in traditional agriculture.[2]

No doubt a lack of economic knowledge breeds doctrines. It has been so with respect to the contributions that agriculture can make to growth. Some of these doctrines are entrenched political dogmas. Some are only the defunct ideas of economists. One can show that these doctrines are wrong, and thus clear the way for a useful conception of this problem. Hopefully too, given time, it may not be altogether naïve to believe that the trumpets of economic analysis may bring down the walls of political dogma.

The more important of these doctrines lead to mistaken answers to the question: what is the role of agriculture in

2. In his Marshall Lectures at the University of Cambridge as they appear in "The Profitability of Investment," *Economic Journal, 69* (December 1959), Professor E. Lundberg, with fine restraint, discusses these and other limitations of macro-growth models. Also see F. A. Lutz and D. C. Hague, eds., *The Theory of Capital,* Proceedings of a Conference of the International Economic Association (London, Macmillan, 1961), Ch. I.

economic growth? The doctrinal answers run as follows: the opportunity for growth from agriculture is among the least attractive of the sources of growth; agriculture can provide a substantial part of the capital that is required to mount industrialization in poor countries; it also can provide an unlimited supply of labor for industry; it can even provide much labor at zero opportunity costs because a considerable part of the labor force in agriculture is redundant in the sense that its marginal productivity is zero; farmers are not responsive to normal economic incentives but instead often respond perversely, with the implication that the supply curve of farm products is backward sloping; and large farms are required in order to produce farm products at minimum costs.

A LEGACY OF DOCTRINES

To build where there are obsolete structures one must first demolish and remove them, which can be costly. In the chapters that follow it will be necessary to examine first one and then another of these doctrines with a view to showing that each is based at best on some half-truths and is a misleading conception of the underlying economic issues that matter. Since some of the more important of these doctrines are a legacy of earlier economic thought, it may be helpful to consider them briefly as a part of the setting of the problem at hand.

The physiocratic and classical legacy with respect to agriculture has been the source of several economic doctrines which have fared badly. The physiocrats built a system on the axiom that agriculture alone is productive, for it yields, so they believed, the subsistence of its workers, the earnings of its entrepreneurs, and a surplus (a "third rent"), while industry and trade are sterile. The classical economists put together a magnificent dynamics[3] based on the accumulation of capital, the Malthusian population principle, and a historical law projecting diminishing returns in agriculture. In their treatment, agriculture is dependent upon a fixed supply of land. Then, as the demand for food increases, rent from land rises, absorbing some of the fruits of economic progress and enriching land owners. Marx rejected the population principle of Malthus but accepted Ricardian rent. An important neglected tenet of Marx is that the costs of agricultural products fall as the size of the production unit in agriculture increases, comparable to the decreasing costs which the classical economists attribute to manufacturing.[4] While always respectful of classical thought, Marshall turned his genius to the building of more practical analytical tools. He did take Henry George to task but did not free himself from the historical dictates of Ricardian rent. Marshall believed that cheaper transportation and the opening of new lands were only temporarily postponing the ultimate further rise of land rent.

None of the tenets of these doctrines pertaining to agriculture has stood the test of time. Except for a mere hand-

3. This phrase is from William J. Baumol, *Economic Dynamics* (New York, Macmillan, 1951), Ch. 2. The classical economists referred to here are "those writers on economic theory who worked in England during and after the time of Malthus and before the time of John Stuart Mill."

4. David Mitrany, *Marx Against the Peasant* (Chapel Hill, University of North Carolina Press, 1951).

ful of agrarian fundamentalists,[5] no one now believes, as the physiocrats did, that agriculture is the only ultimate source of a surplus. A belief in a historical law of diminishing returns that holds uniquely for agriculture still persists among some conservationists, biologists, and demographers. The distinction, so precious to the classical economists, between agriculture and manufacturing in the underlying cost conditions as economic growth takes place is contrary to too many facts. The same adverse conclusion applies to the Marxian tenet that ever-larger farms will necessarily reduce the costs of agricultural products. There is no logical basis for these doctrines. They must rest on empirical findings, and by that test they are found wanting.

There is also a more recent legacy. One of these is rooted in the economic thinking associated with the mass unemployment of the Great Depression. It is the concept of "disguised unemployment" which was extended to countries that have little or no industry, and in the transition it gave birth to the doctrine that a considerable fraction of the labor in agriculture in these countries has a marginal productivity of zero value. To clear away the debris of this doctrine will require a substantial chapter. The roots of the notion, which appears in some of the literature on land reform, that rent performs no useful economic function go back in part to the "unearned component" in Ricardian rent and in part to the twist Marx gave to Ricardian rent. As one might have anticipated, the suppression of rent in allocating farm land is especially evident in a Soviet-type economy. When it comes to modernizing agriculture, much is made of factor indivisi-

5. These fundamentalists do not belong to the "agricultural fundamentalism" about which J. S. Davis took so much umbrage in an essay republished in his *On Agricultural Policy, 1926–1938* (Food Research Institute, Stanford University, 1939).

bilities in farming, of which the farm tractor is the symbol. But it will not be difficult to show that the tractor and others in this class are pseudo-indivisibilities.

ISSUES TO BE PUT ASIDE

Before turning to the unsettled economic questions related to growth from agriculture on which this study concentrates, a few words are required to explain why several related economic issues are not considered. There are three that rank high in this connection, namely (1) the relatively low rate of increase in the demand for farm products as income rises, (2) the effects of the economic instability of a growing economy upon agriculture, and (3) the adaptation of the agricultural sector to growth in high income countries.

The advance in knowledge about consumption, including the demand for farm products, has been a major landmark of recent economic studies. Theory to treat the consumption function has been clarified.[6] Estimates of the price and income elasticities of demand, especially for farm products, have converged, and they have settled the main questions about the demand for farm products that arise in connection with growth. Although there has long been empirical support for the inference that the price elasticity of the demand for most farm products is relatively low in high income countries, satisfactory estimates of the income elasticity of the demand for these products are a fairly recent achievement. Engel's law is of longer standing of course, and although it was derived from only a few statistics they did show that the income elasticity of the demand for food could be less than

6. On this matter, see esp. Milton Friedman, *A Theory of the Consumption Function* (Princeton, Princeton University Press for the National Bureau of Economic Research, 1957).

1.0. But until recently there had been no comprehension of the importance of rising per capita income associated with growth and of the declining income elasticity of the demand for farm foods over time as a consequence of such growth. Less than two decades ago there was still some intellectual excitement in attempting to estimate the income elasticity of farm-produced foods. To have placed it at 0.25 for the United States during the early 1940s still had the appearance of a risky venture.[7] Studies since then, based on broad statistical coverage using modern techniques of analysis, have not only supported this particular estimate but have established a large family of estimates that cover all major classes of farm-produced foods. Moreover, they are now available for many countries with large differences in per capita income. It is noteworthy that economic knowledge about demand and changes in demand over time is far better than that about supply. The apparent theoretical and practical reasons for this difference in the state of economic knowledge have been dealt with elsewhere.[8]

To be sure, as per capita income rises it increases the demand for farm foods relatively more in low than in high income countries (leaving population growth aside). The reason for this important difference is based on the firmly established fact that there are high income countries in which the income elasticity of the demand for farm foods is approaching zero and there are low income countries in which it is still about 0.9.

A summary of Goreux's estimates of the income elasticity

7. This comment refers to the author's estimate, which appeared in his *Agriculture in an Unstable Economy* (New York, McGraw-Hill, 1945), p. 68.

8. Theodore W. Schultz, "Reflections on Agricultural Production, Output and Supply," *Journal of Farm Economics, 38* (August 1956).

of the demand for farm foods in different parts of the world shows the range and magnitude of these differences:[9]

Asia and Far East (excluding Japan)	0.9
Near East and Africa (excluding South Africa)	0.7
Latin America (excluding Argentina and Uruguay)	0.6
Japan	0.6
Mediterranean Europe	0.55
European Economic Community	0.5
Other Western Europe	0.2
North America	0.16

In view of the many relevant studies of the demand for farm products and the wide use being made of their findings, it should not be necessary to enter upon any extended treatment of the changing role of the demand for farm foods as incomes rise over time.

The problems associated with the economic instability that is inherent in economic growth are put aside for the following reasons. The type of mass unemployment that inundated major industrial countries during the thirties can be pre-

9. Dr. L. M. Goreux has done pioneering work in developing a worldwide picture of the income elasticities of demand for farm-produced foods. See his "Income and Food Consumption," FAO [Food and Agriculture Organization] *Monthly Bulletin of Agricultural Economics and Statistics, 9,* No. 10 (October 1960). See also *Review of Food Consumption Surveys* by FAO (Rome, July 1958) and L. M. Goreux, *Income Elasticity of the Demand for Food,* Economic Commission for Europe in cooperation with FAO (June 22, 1959, mimeo.). Most useful is an exhaustive FAO *Bibliography on Demand Analysis and Projections* (1959, mimeo., 167 pages); a 1960 *Supplement* (mimeo., 98 pages), and a 1961 *Supplement* (mimeo., 62 pages). For a summary of L. M. Goreux estimates, see *Agricultural Commodities Projections for 1970,* FAO *Commodity Review 1962, Special Supplement* (Rome, 1962). The above estimates are from Table 12, based on farm value during the period 1957–59. Also see H. E. Buchholz, G. G. Judge, and V. I. West, *A Summary of the Selected Estimated Behavior Relationship for Agricultural Products in the U.S.* (Urbana, University of Illinois College of Agriculture, AERR 57, October 1962).

vented by monetary and fiscal measures, and it seems unlikely that these countries will fail to prevent such mass unemployment in any foreseeable future. The more "normal" booms and recessions of the business cycle have also been dampened and, as a consequence, not only is the flow of personal income steadier but the expectations of consumers are also modified, for consumers have come to look increasingly upon the fluctuations as if they were transitory movements in their income. Thus it would appear that the demand of consumers, including that for food and for the farm products entering into food, has been measurably stabilized.[10] Meanwhile, there has been a proliferation of programs to stabilize farm product prices chiefly by means of price supports. These supports have altered significantly the short-run movements of farm prices within particular countries. But the effects of price supports upon the longer-run movements and structure of farm product prices are far from clear. The contributions of a well-conceived program of *forward prices* for agriculture[11] in improving the efficiency of farm product prices as incentives to guide and reward farmers are still real and significant. Economic changes that have occurred since forward prices were originally proposed have not made the proposal obsolete though the widespread misuse of support prices has created a presumption that governments are not yet capable of authorizing and administering a program of forward prices that would meet the necessary conditions for their success.

10. Robert S. Firch, "Stabilization of the United States Economy and Stability of Farm Income" (unpublished Ph.D. dissertation, University of Chicago, 1963).

11. See D. Gale Johnson, *Forward Prices for Agriculture* (Chicago, University of Chicago Press, 1947), and the author's *Agriculture in an Unstable Economy* and *The Economic Organization of Agriculture* (New York, McGraw-Hill, 1953).

A major new problem has arisen in a number of high income countries in which the agricultural sector has been most successful in adopting and using modern factors of production. It is the problem of adapting agriculture with its high rate of increase in labor productivity to a high income economy in which the demand for farm products is of slow growth. It becomes an acute problem when the labor force required for farming begins to decline at a substantial rate and many of the farm people who leave agriculture are poorly prepared in skills and schooling for nonfarm jobs which, to compound the difficulty, are hard to find because of substantial unemployment. But countries still saddled with traditional agriculture are not up against this particular problem. It is not treated in this study for the simple reason that it is not germane to the economic issues underlying the transformation of traditional agriculture.[12]

UNSETTLED QUESTIONS

In determining the opportunities in agriculture for economic growth, it will be necessary to resolve three unsettled questions: (1) Can low income communities increase

12. Moreover, there is a considerable body of economic thought on this adaptation problem. A major part of the author's *The Economic Organization of Agriculture* is devoted to it. Earl O. Heady, *Agricultural Policy Under Economic Development* (Ames, Iowa, Iowa State University Press, 1962) and Dale E. Hathaway, *Government and Agriculture: Public Policy in a Democratic Society* (New York, Macmillan, 1963) are both important contributions. The underlying welfare problem, which arises in this and in other sectors, is treated in the author's "A Policy to Redistribute Losses from Economic Progress," *Journal of Farm Economics, 43* (August 1961), and also appears in *Labor Mobility and Population in Agriculture* (Ames, Iowa, Iowa State University Press, 1962). A policy statement by the Committee for Economic Development, *An Adaptive Program for Agriculture* (New York, 1962), as the title implies, is addressed to this problem.

agricultural production substantially by an efficient allocation of the agricultural factors of production presently at their disposal? (2) Which agricultural factors of production are primarily responsible for the large differences among countries in the success of the agricultural sector in contributing to economic growth? (3) Under what conditions does it pay to invest in agriculture? The first and the third questions raise fundamental economic issues, and the treatment of them is the heart of this study. The second question serves mainly to orient the analysis.

Turning to the first, how much additional agricultural production can be achieved in low income countries by improving the allocative efficiency of farming, that is, allocating existing land, structures, equipment, and farm people (farm workers and farmers) more efficiently? Two major chapters are devoted to this question because of the widely held belief that the agricultural sector in poor countries is generally quite inefficient in using the factors at hand. The hypothesis advanced in this study is to the contrary, namely, that the agricultural sector in a large class of poor countries is relatively efficient in using the factors of production at its disposal.

To what extent do the observable differences in agricultural production among countries depend upon differences in land, or in material capital, or in farm people? The conventional answer used to be "land," to which is now added "the tractor." But these two explain only a few of the differences in agricultural production. This study supports the proposition that differences in land are least important, differences in the quality of material capital are of substantial importance, and differences in the capabilities of farm people are most important in explaining the differences in the amount and rate of increase of agricultural production.

No small part of the problem of understanding agriculture as a source of economic growth is burdened by the legacy of ideas about land.[13] Farm land has two components, a natural endowment component and a capital structure component. The latter is a consequence of past investments. Theorists implicitly often mean by land only its natural endowment. But it is for the most part an empty concept because so many of the differences in the productivity of farm land are man-made. Investments in land over time do matter. In addition, production of factors that substitute for land is of increasing importance.

But, all told, differences in land are not a strong explanatory variable of trends in agricultural production. Nor are the differences in the *quantity* of material capital of the conventional sort employed in agriculture, measured by the share of the income that is earned by such capital at factor costs. However, the *quality* of the material capital employed in agriculture does matter significantly. The quality of such capital depends upon the extent to which it embodies the knowledge of the agricultural sciences. But the key variable in explaining the differences in agricultural production is the human agent, i.e., the differences in the level of the acquired capabilities of farm people.

At this point it will be helpful to see what is happening in agriculture. Even a sketch of trends in agricultural production in different parts of the world will aid in clarifying the issues under consideration.

Western Europe has been doing exceedingly well in agricultural production. This old, crowded workshop with a population density much greater than Asia's, and with a poor endowment of farm land generally, has been increasing its

13. See the author's essay, "Land in Economic Growth," *Modern Land Policy* (Urbana, University of Illinois Press, 1958), Ch. 2.

agricultural production at a rate that would have been thought impossible only a couple of decades ago. Italy, Austria, and Greece, for example, with less arable land per capita than India and with farm land inferior to India's, have increased agricultural production at a rate of 3.0, 3.3, and 5.7 per cent per year respectively compared to 2.1 for India.[14] Moreover, in Northwest Europe between 1950 and 1959 employment in agriculture declined over a fifth and the productivity of labor in agriculture rose by a half.[15] New land obviously is not the explanation. It is the same old endowment of mostly poor land. If anything, the total area devoted to arable farming has been declining somewhat. Improvement in the quality of farm capital, yes; a farm people capable of using modern factors, yes; large-scale farming, no.

In many ways Israel also is European. The ratio of population to land suitable for farming is high. The land is not of high quality and no one would have rated the prospects for agriculture as bright. Yet between 1952 and 1959 production more than doubled although farm employment rose only a fourth.[16] Again land has not been the main source of this growth. Modern factors of production have been important. The people who entered upon agriculture were not skilled at farming, for they were mainly nonfarm people, but most of them had a good deal of schooling. The *kibbut-*

14. Based on 1952–59 agricultural production. See FAO, *Agricultural Commodities Projections for 1970,* Table M18.

15. Ten countries are included: Austria, Belgium, Denmark, France, West Germany, Ireland, Netherlands, Norway, Sweden, and the United Kingdom. The period is 1950–59. Source: *Agricultural Commodities Projections for 1970,* Table M13.

16. A. L. Gaathon, *Capital Stock, Employment and Output in Israel, 1950–1959,* Speculative Studies, No. 1 (Jerusalem, Bank of Israel, 1961), Appendix B and C.

zim (large farm) has done well but it has been less efficient than the *moshavim* (small).[17]

Latin America presents two very different pictures. One is exemplified by Mexico and the other by Argentina, Chile, and Uruguay. Agricultural production in Mexico has been increasing at the unusually high rate of 7.1 per cent per year.[18] The lesson to be learned from what Mexico has accomplished is especially germane to many low income countries seeking to develop a modern economy. Mexico entered upon this rapid growth very recently. The foundations for growth were not laid by an earlier, gradual development spread over many decades. Nor has Mexico made the mistake of some low income countries of industrializing at the expense of agriculture, or of simply neglecting agriculture until an industrial base had been established. Mexico is one of the few countries that has been modernizing both industry and agriculture and winning large increases in national income from both.

As yet, the economic growth of Mexico has not received the attention it deserves and so the economic basis of this success has not been fully established. Mexican economists attribute much of it to the land reform.[19] This surely was important in setting the political and economic stage for economic progress. But land reform did not change the natural endowment. Farm land in Mexico is inferior, for example, to that of the Argentine. Many *ejidos* (a set of small

17. Ezra Sadan, "Agricultural Settlements in Israel: A Study in Resource Allocation" (unpublished Ph.D. dissertation in economics, University of Chicago, 1962).

18. From FAO, *Agricultural Commodities Projections for 1970,* Table M18, for the years 1952–59.

19. Edmundo Flores, *Tratado de Economia Agricola* (Mexico, Fundo de Cultura Economica, 1961).

farms from the breaking up of a large "plantation type" farm) were established by the land reform; they have not done well. But many farms outside the *ejidos* have done exceedingly well. The government not only invested in dams and irrigation facilities but also, with assistance from the Rockefeller Foundation, in the agricultural sciences. Many modern agricultural factors have been adopted. Roads and communications facilities have been much improved. But the skills and schooling of farm people appear to have lagged, and they are, so it seems, becoming a limitational factor in growth.

Agricultural production in Chile has increased at only 1.6 per cent per year,[20] and in the Argentine and Uruguay it has stagnated. Yet the high quality of the land in the Argentine for growing alfalfa, corn, and some other crops is renowned. Parts of Argentina are comparable to the best of Iowa, while the natural potential of Chile for producing a wide range of farm products is much like that of California. The advance in the agricultural sciences in the United States and elsewhere is more applicable to these countries than to most. Moreover, no longer than two or three decades ago they were fairly abreast in the use of the then best factors of production. But absentee ownership of land and large land holdings persist. Economic incentives to guide and reward farmers have been woefully inefficient. Agricultural stagnation has settled over the countryside.

When it comes to total agricultural production, Asia and the Far East overshadow any other region, exceeding by a wide margin the combined output of Europe and Latin America. Yet there is far from enough food. As is well known, there are three times as many mouths to be fed. The break-

20. See footnote 18 for the source of this estimate.

through in agricultural production centers on Japan. China, despite its massive program to expand agricultural production, is in real trouble. The results of India's many efforts to increase the output of this sector are encouraging but far from impressive. The picture can best be shown by a comparison of developments in Japan and India.

Agricultural production in Japan has been increasing at a rate of 4.6 per cent per year while in India, as has already been noted, it has been rising at only 2.1.[21] If differences in farm land had been a strong factor, the ratio of agricultural growth should have been the other way around. On a per capita basis, India has six times as much agricultural land as Japan.[22] The land of India as a natural endowment is also of better quality. Even in terms of irrigated area, India has nearly three times as much as Japan, measured on a per capita basis.[23] But total agricultural production per acre in Japan has become fully eight times that of India.[24] There is no doubt that the quality of material agricultural factors employed in Japan is far better than that used in India. But more important still are the high level of farming skills and the amount of schooling that the farm people of Japan have acquired compared to the low level of skills and general illiteracy that still prevail in rural India.

The success in agricultural production in the United States is dramatized by surpluses, exceedingly large exports, and all manner of public programs to reduce output. Even

21. See footnote 18.

22. Lester R. Brown, *An Economic Analysis of Far Eastern Agriculture,* Foreign Agricultural Economic Report, No. 2 (U.S. Department of Agriculture, November 1961), Table 5.

23. Brown, *Economic Analysis,* Tables 3 and 7.

24. Brown, *Economic Analysis,* Table 16. In value terms based on 1958 world prices the 1957–59 average annual production of Japan has been estimated at $274 per acre and that of India at $33.

so, between 1940 and 1961 farm output rose 56 per cent while harvested cropland declined about 10 per cent (36 million acres less!) and the labor force employed in farming declined by about two-fifths. The productivity of labor in agriculture, as a consequence, rose at nearly three times the rate of labor in industry. Nor is the end in sight, for surely agriculture in the United States, mainly because of its success, is caught in a massive disequilibrium with all too many resources, consisting primarily of too much labor employed in producing farm products. It is of course true that the natural endowment of farm land is large and much of it is high in quality. But it was always so. Yet, once settlement had been essentially completed as it had been prior to World War I, there came a period when agricultural production hardly increased at all. The many efforts to expand agricultural production during World War I made clear that expansion was becoming difficult. The farm output of 1917–19 was only 6 per cent more than that of 1910–12. The upsurge began toward the beginning of the thirties when the effects of the slowly accumulating advance of the agricultural sciences upon production were becoming significant. The investment in farm people through agricultural extension activities and more schooling made for the adoption of these modern factors and their effective use by farmers.

But it would be a mistake to infer from what has been said about farm land and growth from agriculture that the efficient allocation of land in farming and investments in structures that became a part of the land do not count. The suppression of rent, which is now not uncommon, impairs its allocative function and, as will be shown later, can do much harm. It would be correct to infer, however, from the setting of the problem of growth from agriculture proposed here that improvements in the *quality* of the material factors employed in farming and in the capabilities of farm people count much more than land.

An alternate approach to the problem of growth from agriculture, which is more useful analytically than that implied in either of the first two questions, is to determine the price of additional income streams that can be had by increasing the stock of reproducible factors employed in agriculture. In using this approach, it will be convenient for the sake of simplification to assume that there are only two types of agricultural communities. In one, agricultural production is based wholly on long-established traditional factors of production. In the other, some modern agricultural factors are employed and additional ones are being adopted. Thus in the first model the assumption will be that the only source of additional income from agricultural production is from increases in the quantity of traditional factors of precisely the same sort that have been used for many decades. This model implies the hypothesis that the price of additional income streams from this source is relatively high, so high that there is no incentive to save in order to invest in such agricultural factors. The other model, to be used in examining the behavior of farmers where substantial growth is being obtained from agriculture, implies the hypothesis that the price of additional income streams from this source is relatively low.

The critical economic question, therefore, becomes: under what conditions does it pay to invest in agriculture? The implication is, from what has already been said, that it will not pay unless the man who farms has the opportunity and incentive to transform the traditional agriculture of his forebears.

2 ATTRIBUTES OF TRADITIONAL AGRICULTURE

The approach of this study is to explain the production behavior of farmers who are bound by traditional agriculture and then to determine whether it is profitable to transform this type of agriculture by means of investment. The presumption is that when farmers are limited to traditional factors of production they reach a point after which they can make little or no contribution to economic growth because there are few significant inefficiencies in the allocation of factors, the removal of which would increase current production, and because investment made to increase the stock of traditional factors would be a costly source of economic growth. These two propositions, i.e., efficient allocation of factors and a low rate of return to investment at the margin, will be formulated as hypotheses that can be tested empirically. There is then another presumption to the effect that there are alternative agricultural factors which would be relatively cheap sources of economic growth. In adopting this approach the first question is: what are the critical attributes of traditional agriculture?

The picture that comes to mind at once is of farming as a way of life based on long-established folkways. This view suggests that traditional agriculture is essentially a cultural characterization of the way particular people live. Another picture puts into focus the institutional arrangements pertaining to ownership of land, the legal basis of tenure, and the extent to which production is for home consumption. Still another concentrates on the technical properties of agricultural factors of production. What then are the *critical* attributes? It should not come as a surprise that an economic conception of traditional agriculture cannot be formulated rigorously in terms of cultural attributes, institutional arrangements, or technical properties of factors of production. Even a cursory examination of these characteristics will make this clear.

The distinction between a face-to-face, personal, i.e., folk society and other types is an exceedingly useful one for many purposes. Economists generally appear to believe that farm people as a matter of course belong to a folk society. But there are many farm people who are members of an impersonal community often called an "urban" society. Folk societies and agricultural production based on traditional factors are independent categories. When they are applied to the same community, they sometimes agree and sometimes disagree. The most that can be said is that a folk society often *is* traditional agriculture. Nevertheless, a folk society and traditional agriculture are not necessarily compatibles, and by no means is all traditional agriculture to be found in folk societies. For this reason, the cultural attributes of a folk society do not provide a rigorous basis for identifying traditional agriculture.

The niggardliness of agriculture in poor communities is frequently attributed to particular cultural values. These values relate to work, thrift, industriousness, and aspirations for a higher standard of living. They are then used to explain why there is so little economic progress and why particular economic development programs are unsuccessful in practice. As a rule, however, it is not necessary to appeal to differences in such cultural values, because a simple economic explanation will suffice.

Consider, first, the attitude toward work. It is said again and again that people in poor communities do not care to work long and hard. Presumably they prefer to be idle instead. Thus, the "leisure" associated with such idleness is valued more highly than the increase in production that could be had from more work. The inference that follows is that these people value this kind of idleness too highly. But what is not reckoned is their lack of vigor and stamina to work hard and long and the low marginal return to additional work. Another variant of this view relates to the effects of schooling upon the willingness of those with some schooling to do manual agricultural work. Even a little schooling, it is said, turns the youth of poor agricultural communities against farm work. But those who make these observations generally fail to indicate the differences in earnings from farm work and from other work open to those who have some schooling.[1] While particular class or caste arrangements af-

1. See Kusum Nair, *Blossoms in the Dust* (London, Duckworth, 1961), Ch. XXI and also repeatedly elsewhere throughout the book. The author spent a year traveling throughout villages in India. She is a resourceful and keen observer and, what is rare, writes with much clarity. It is a rewarding book to read, although one wishes that, in her

fect choices and the mobility of labor and the adaptive capacity of an economy to changing economic conditions, it does not follow that people who belong to a class or caste which does farm work have a penchant for being idle. It could be that the preferences and motives for working are essentially the same for a wide array of agricultural communities. If so, traditional agriculture is not a consequence of particular farm people having preferences of loafers but what appears to be loafing is a consequence of the low marginal productivity of labor.

There is also much confusion about differences among people with respect to thrift. It is often alleged that there is a lack of thrift in poor, stagnant agricultural communities and that this is a consequence of the cultural attributes of the farm people in these communities. They simply will not save enough to get ahead. And why not? They are supposedly subject to particular cultural constraints that cause them to indulge in much wasteful consumption, notably when marriage and death occur and when festivities come along. One might ask, how else could they tolerate the otherwise harsh and drab existence which is their lot? To call all this "wasteful consumption" is an odd twist of language. Nor should sight be lost of another and quite contrary view, namely, that agricultural people are very frugal, often all too frugal in the consumption they allow themselves and especially when it comes to attending to the welfare of their children.

But thrift can be treated straightway as economic behavior.

---

comments on schooling and attitudes toward manual work, differences in earnings from manual work (in agriculture and fishing) and other jobs had been ascertained. Also, in the comments on the failure of some classes of cultivators to take advantage of water for irrigation, the question that is not answered is: what would have been the costs of such water set against the return from its use?

The question to ask is: what are the rewards to them for saving more of their meager income? The hypothesis advanced in this study is that the rate of return on such savings when they are invested in the traditional factors of production is exceedingly low. Should this hypothesis be consistent with the facts, there would be little or no inducement to save.

The virtue of being industrious is much stressed in criticizing the economic performance of people in poor communities. This means that the presumed penchant for idleness and for wasteful consumption is treated as a valid indication that the people are not sufficiently industrious. It was once fashionable to say in this connection that they lack the economic virtues of the Protestant Ethic. Such a view of the source of the differences in economic behavior under consideration is a naïve notion of cultural differences. For example, when it comes to being industrious, including work and thrift, it is hard for even an industrious Protestant to fault the behavior of the Guatemalan Indians described with such care and thoroughness by Sol Tax in *Penny Capitalism*.[2]

The implication to be drawn from these observations is not that cultural differences do not matter but that differences in work, thrift, and industry related to economic activities can be handled as economic variables. It is not necessary to appeal to cultural differences to explain *particular* work and thrift behavior because economic factors provide a satisfactory explanation. Incentives to work more than these people do are weak because the marginal productivity of labor is very low; and incentives to save more than they do are weak because the marginal productivity of capital is also very low.

2. See pp. 41–44 and 90–94 for further discussion of this book.

Thus, however relevant the cultural attributes are in examining some important classes of problems, they do not provide a basis for distinguishing between traditional and other types of agriculture. Similarly, such a basis is not to be found in the differences in particular institutional arrangements, for example in whether farms are under resident or absentee ownership, whether they are small or large, whether they are private or public enterprises, and whether the production is for home consumption or for sale. Although these institutional arrangements are not a key to traditional agriculture, they are nonetheless important in determining how to modernize agriculture by means of investment. They will therefore be considered in some detail in later chapters. Differences in the technical attributes of capital and labor were also referred to earlier. But, since traditional agriculture is compatible with a wide range of farming skills and of capital goods used in farming, differences in these technical attributes of agricultural factors are in this respect on the same footing as the cultural attributes and institutional arrangements already mentioned, in that they do not provide a satisfactory basis for determining what is and what is not traditional agriculture.

AN ECONOMIC CONCEPTION

In this study traditional agriculture will be treated as a particular type of economic equilibrium. Viewed *ex post,* it is an equilibrium at which agriculture gradually arrives over a long period, provided particular conditions prevail. Viewed in prospect, an agricultural sector that is not now of this type will under the same conditions over a long period eventually arrive at the equilibrium that characterizes traditional agriculture. The critical conditions underlying this type of equilibrium, either historically or in the future, are as follows: (1) the state of the arts remains constant, (2) the state of preference and motives for holding and acquiring sources of income remains constant, and (3) both of these states remain constant long enough for marginal preferences and motives for acquiring agricultural factors as sources of income to arrive at an equilibrium with the marginal productivity of these sources viewed as an investment in permanent income streams and with net savings approaching zero.

It is also important to be clear on the economic components that are variables in this conception of traditional agriculture. In the process of reaching this type of equilibrium, the stock of material factors of production and the labor force are the principal variables. By means of investment or disinvestment the composition and the size of the stock of reproducible material factors can be changed. New land can be acquired and settled and structures that become a part of the land can be varied. There also may be some gains from further division of labor that are achieved during the process of reaching this type of equilibrium.

The particular economic equilibrium represented by traditional agriculture is fundamentally based on the state of the arts underlying the supply of reproducible factors of production, the state of preference and motives underlying the demand for sources of income, and the period of time during which these two states remain constant. In the case of the state of the arts the following *ex post* specifications are essential. The agricultural factors that farmers employ have been used by them and their forebears for a long time and none of these factors meanwhile has been altered significantly as a consequence of learning from experience. Nor have any new agricultural factors been introduced. Thus what is known by farmers about the factors they use has been known by farm people in the community for one or more generations. For a long time nothing new has been learned either from trial and error or from other sources. Consequently the state of the arts is constant, which meets one of the classical assumptions though it is a much misused assumption in studying modern economic growth.

Although the knowledge that is a part of the state of the arts is passed on from father to son by word of mouth and by demonstration, this does not mean that what is handed down is not authentic knowledge. In general, farmers who are limited to traditional agricultural factors are more secure in what they know about the factors they use than farmers who are adopting and learning how to use new factors of production. The new types of risk and uncertainty about the yield inherent in factors embodying an advance in knowledge are of real concern to farmers. They could be of critical importance to farmers who are producing so little that there is barely enough production for survival. But since traditional agriculture is not introducing new factors, new elements of risk and uncertainty do not appear; they arise only when the transformation gets under way. What matters here is that the state of the arts is in fact known, established, and given in the case of traditional agriculture, and that the supply price of reproducible factors rises as the quantity of these factors increases.

That the basic preferences and motives under consideration may remain constant over long periods is highly plausible, if for no other reason than that it is difficult to conceive of developments that could change them. As agriculture approaches the particular equilibrium of traditional agriculture, the marginal productivity of investment in additional agricultural factors continues to decline. There then comes a point when the rate of return is so low that there is no longer any incentive to save for additional investment in these factors. From what already has been stated, no new agricultural factors are being introduced and the productivity of all of the factors used has been known for a long time. There is accordingly virtually perfect knowledge about the marginal rate of return to investment in agriculture, and this state of knowledge has existed long enough for an equilibrium to have become established between savings and investment, or between the demand for and the supply of agricultural factors as a source of income.

HOW TRANSITORY IS TRADITIONAL AGRICULTURE?

Once traditional agriculture has become established, is it a persistent type of equilibrium, not readily subject to change, or is it transitory? In examining this question, it will be convenient first to consider factors other than changes in the state of the arts and in the state of preferences.

If the value of farm products were to rise, the marginal returns to agricultural factors would increase, and this would induce some additional investment in them. A new transport facility that reduced the costs of transporting farm products to the ultimate consumer could have the same effect, i.e., increase the value of farm products somewhat and the investment in agricultural factors in response. An irrigation facility, or a reduction in the costs of any agricultural factor that farmers purchased, could bring about similar changes. But in all of these, if the state of the arts in agriculture remained unchanged, it would be only a matter of time before the particular equilibrium characteristic of traditional agriculture would re-establish itself.

Preference and motive underlying the demand for the

sources of income streams, as already noted, appear to be highly stable. For reasons that will be considered later in this study, they may be essentially the same for a wide array of communities. But the state of the arts is another matter. It is undoubtedly a key variable in explaining modern economic growth whether the source of such growth is from agriculture or from the rest of the economy.

Yet it is possible that traditional agriculture has certain strong built-in resistors to any changes in the existing state of the arts. The concept of traditional agriculture implies long-established routines with respect to all production activities. Introducing a new factor of production would mean not only breaking with the past but coping with a problem, because the production possibilities of the new factor will be subject to risks and uncertainties as yet unknown. It is therefore not sufficient merely to adopt the new factors and reap the larger return; learning from experience what new risks and uncertainties are inherent in these factors is also entailed. The hypothesis bearing on this matter to be set forth and tried later is that the rate at which farmers who have settled into a traditional agriculture accept a new factor of production depends upon its profit, with due allowance for risk and uncertainty, and in this respect the response is similar to that observed by farmers in modern agriculture.

THE PUZZLE

Suppose it were true that not much additional income could be had from a better allocation of the existing stock of traditional factors of production. This assumption does not rule out some small gains from this source, but it does imply that growth opportunities in this direction are unimportant.[3] Suppose, further, that it were also true that investment to increase somewhat the stock of traditional factors of production would produce a very low rate of return.[4] Here, too, there could be some imperfections in the way the capital "market" functions, which could be corrected, and if this were achieved some additional investment would be forthcoming. Yet the increase in income from such measures would not open the door wide for economic growth. Lastly, then, suppose there were some reproducible factors of production in other communities that differ from the traditional factors on which a particular community is dependent and that these differences make them both more productive and profitable. Why is it that farm people now dependent upon traditional agriculture do not take advantage of these more productive and more profitable factors?

The puzzle underlying this question is ever so perplexing in the case of Panajachel, Guatemala, a community to be

3. Even in fairly advanced countries that harbor many misallocations of resources, as has been the case in recent years in Chile, the elimination of these misallocations "would raise the national welfare by no more that 15 per cent." This is the conclusion of Arnold C. Harberger from his studies of the Chilean economy, "Using the Resources at Hand More Effectively," *American Economic Review* (Papers and Proceedings), *49* (May 1959), 134–46.

4. Although the Chilean economy is technically far from poor, another reference to Chile is instructive in showing that a low rate of return to investment may explain much of the poor growth of the industrial sector. Tom E. Davis, who has estimated "the rate of return on investment (including capital gains) on the average of the common shares of the 307 actively traded corporations on the Santiago Stock Exchange over the period 1929–59," found that the (real) rate of return to shareholders of these corporations was only 2 per cent per annum. See "The Rate of Return on Capital in Latin-American Economies: With Special Reference to Chile," in testimony prepared for the Hearings on Economic Development in South America, May 10–11, 1962, Subcommittee on Inter-American Economic Relationships of the Joint Economic Committee of the Congress of the United States.

examined in some detail in the next and later chapters. The people are obviously hard working, thrifty, and acute in selling their crops, renting land, and buying things for consumption and production. The community is not an isolated subsistence economy, but is closely integrated into a larger market economy. Yet hoes, axes, and machetes are not replaced by better tools and equipment. There is not even a wheel. Coffee leaves used as fertilizer are not replaced or supplemented by chemical fertilizers. Traditional varieties of corn are not replaced by hybrid seed. Traditional breeds of chickens are not replaced by better hens for producing eggs and broilers for producing meat. The traders and firms in the towns that serve this community are not offering for sale any of the superior factors. If one wanted to plan a community like Panajachel that would go on for decades without any change in the state of arts on which it was dependent, it would strike one as impossible within the market economy of Guatemala. Yet Panajachel has been doing the "impossible" in this respect for generations. That is the puzzle.

3 THE ALLOCATIVE EFFICIENCY OF TRADITIONAL AGRICULTURE

The economic acumen of people in poor agricultural communities is generally maligned. It is widely held that they save and invest too little of their income in view of what capital earns, that they pay no heed to changes in prices, and that they disregard normal economic incentives at every turn. For these and other reasons, it is frequently said they do badly in using the factors they have. But is this true? The aim of this chapter is to examine the efficiency with which farmers within traditional agriculture allocate the factors at their disposal.

THE ECONOMIC EFFICIENCY HYPOTHESIS

There is, as has already been noted, a large class of poor agricultural communities in which people have been doing the same things for generations. Changes in products and factors have not crowded in on them. For them neither consumption nor production is studded with new gadgets.

The factors of production on which they depend are known through long experience and are in this sense "traditional." While the communities in this class differ appreciably one from another in the quantity of factors they possess, in what they grow, in the arts of cultivation, and culturally, they have one fundamental attribute in common: they have for years not experienced any significant alterations in the state of the arts. This means simply that farmers of this class continue year after year to cultivate the same type of land, sow the same crops, use the same techniques of production, and bring the same skills to bear in agricultural production. To examine the allocative behavior of these farmers, the following hypothesis is proposed:

> *There are comparatively few significant inefficiencies in the allocation of the factors of production in traditional agriculture.*

The factors of production under these circumstances consist of traditional factors, and the hypothesis is restricted to those factors at the disposal of the people of a particular community. It should be made clear that not all poor agricultural communities have the economic attributes of traditional agriculture. Some are excluded on the ground that they have been subject to change. Any community that has experienced a significant alteration to which it has not had time to adjust fully is excluded. When a new road or railroad is built, as a rule it takes some years for the communities affected to adapt to it. The economic routine of the affected communities is also disturbed by a new large dam, irrigation canals, structures to control floods and to reduce soil erosion. A serious adversity of nature—a flood or a drought followed by famine—can be a source of disequilibrium. Some poor agricultural communities must be excluded because they have been subject to large political changes, for example by partition, by recruitment of many men into the armed services, or by the destruction of both human and nonhuman resources by war. Large changes in relative prices of products because of outside developments affecting the terms of trade can also upset the quiet economic life of particular communities. In modern times, the most pervasive force disturbing the equilibrium of agricultural communities is the advance in knowledge useful in agricultural production. Any poor agricultural community that is adjusting its production to one or more of these circumstances is excluded from traditional agriculture to which the *efficient but poor hypothesis* applies. The fact that particular communities are excluded because they are making major adjustments in production does not imply that they are inherently inefficient in making the adjustments. The test in that case, however, is different.

Whether one wishes to test or to examine the implications of the proposed hypothesis, it will be necessary to distinguish between an efficient allocation of the stock of factors devoted to current production and an optimum rate of investment to increase the stock of such factors. It will be convenient at this stage, in working with this hypothesis, to assume that the rate of return to investment is given and, whether the rate is low or high, that the total stock of factors can be increased only a little per year. Accordingly, the rate of return can be either low or high, or, if one prefers, the price of additional income streams can be either dear or cheap. The hypothesis at this point pertains only to the allocation of the existing factors in current agricultural production, with the prevailing rate of return to investment given. The question of investment will be considered later.

It may be helpful to mention a few of the implications of

the hypothesis. The principal implication is of course that no appreciable increase in agricultural production is to be had by reallocating the factors at the disposal of farmers who are bound by traditional agriculture. It follows, therefore, that the combination of crops grown, the number of times and depth of cultivation, the time of planting, watering, and harvesting, the combination of hand tools, ditches to carry water to the fields, draft animals and simple equipment—are all made with a fine regard for marginal costs and returns. Implied also is that significant indivisibilities will not show their ugly heads. Product and factor prices will reveal themselves as flexible. Another implication is that an outside expert, however skilled he may be in farm management, will not discover any major inefficiency in the allocation of factors. To the extent that any of these implications are contrary to the observable and relevant facts, the hypothesis here proposed would be under a cloud of doubt.

Mindful of what an outside expert can usefully do that goes beyond a reallocation of existing factors, it must be underscored that in testing this hypothesis it is not permissible to alter the technical properties of the factors of production at the disposal of the community. Nor is it permissible to provide new useful knowledge about superior factors that exist in other communities, that is, provide such knowledge at a cost that would be less than it was formerly. Doing so would alter the costs and the return to the search for information pertaining to alternative economic opportunities. Obviously, the introduction of better varieties of seeds and other technically superior inputs by the expert is precluded in making this test. If the outside expert were successful in these respects, he would alter the established equilibrium that may otherwise have characterized the economic activities of the community being investigated.

Still another implication of this hypothesis is that no productive factor remains unemployed. Each parcel of land is used that can make a net contribution to production, given the existing state of the arts and other available factors. So are irrigation ditches, draft animals, and other reproducible forms of capital. Also, each laborer who wishes and who is capable of doing some useful work is employed. It is of course possible to conceive of exotic technical conditions in agriculture that preclude "full" employment. Workers conceivably could become so numerous as to be in each other's way. There could be indivisibilities in factors of production. But these seem to be paper tigers, for they are not found in this class of agricultural communities. The recent doctrine that agricultural production activities are often such that capable workers contribute nothing to production at the margin—that is, that a part of the agricultural labor force has a marginal productivity of zero value—will be examined in the following chapter. The efficient but poor hypothesis does not imply that the real earnings (production) of labor are not meager. Earnings less than subsistence are not inconsistent with this hypothesis provided there are other sources of income, whether from other factors belonging to workers or from transfers within the family or among families in the community.

In turning to the real world to test the hypothesis here advanced, the main difficulty is the paucity of usable data. The propensity to take any estimates, however weak they may be, and force them into a Cobb-Douglas type of production function, is as a rule a sheer waste of time. Fortunately, some social anthropologists studying particular communities of this type for extended periods have diligently recorded product and factor prices, costs and returns of the major economic activities, and the institutional framework in which production, consumption, savings, and investment occur. Two of these studies—one pertaining to a Guatemalan Indian community and another to an agricultural community in India—are especially useful and relevant. These two studies will now be examined in relation to the proposed hypothesis.

PANAJACHEL, GUATEMALA: VERY POOR BUT EFFICIENT

A classic study by Sol Tax, *Penny Capitalism,*[1] opens with these words: it is "a society which is 'capitalist' on a microscopic scale. There are no machines, no factories, no co-ops or corporations. Every man is his own firm and works ruggedly for himself. Money there is, in small denominations; trade there is, with what men carry on their backs; free entrepreneurs, the impersonal market place, competition—these are in the rural economy." Tax leaves no doubt that this community is very poor, that it is under strong competitive behavior, and that its 800 people are making the most of the factors and techniques of production at their command.[2]

No one ought to be surprised that the people are very poor. Tax puts their poverty this way: they "live without medical aid or drugs, in dirt-floored huts with hardly any furniture, the light only of the fire that smokes up the room, or of a pitch-pine torch or a little tin kerosene lamp; the

1. Originally published by the Smithsonian Institution, Institute of Social Anthropology, Publication No. 16 (Washington, U.S. Government Printing Office, 1953). Reprinted by the University of Chicago Press, 1963.

2. This study is keyed to data covering the period from 1936 to 1941. Professor Tax lived in the community on and off from the autumn of 1935 to the spring of 1941 (see his preface).

mortality rate is high; the diet is meager and most people cannot afford more than a half-pound of meat a week. . . . Schools are almost nonexistent; the children cannot be spared from work in the field. . . . Life is mostly hard work."[3] Tax presents many data measuring the consumer goods and the level and cost of living to support this poignant testimony on the poverty of the community.

Competition is present everywhere in the way products and factors are priced. "All household utensils—pottery, grinding stones, baskets, gourds, china, and so on—and practically all household furnishings such as tables and chairs and mats, must be brought in from other towns. So must many articles of wearing apparel, such as material for skirts and cloaks, hats, sandals, blankets, and carrying bags, as well as cotton and thread for weaving the other things. So must most of the essential foodstuffs: the greater part of the corn, all lime, salt and spices, most of the chile, and most of the meat. . . . To get the money they depend upon the sale of agricultural produce . . . . Onions and garlic, a number of fruits, and coffee are the chief commodities produced for sale."[4] Prices are in every respect highly flexible.

Tax goes on to document the fact that the Indian is "above all else an entrepreneur, a business man," always looking for new means of turning a penny. He buys the goods he can afford with a close regard for price in various markets, he calculates with care the value of his labor in producing crops for sale or for home consumption against his working for hire, and he acts accordingly. He rents and pawns parcels of land with a shrewd eye to the return, and he does likewise in acquiring the few producer goods that he buys from others. All of this business, "may be characterized as *a money econ-*

3. Tax, p. 28.
4. Ibid., pp. 11–12.

omy organized in single households as both consumption and production units, with a strongly developed market which tends to be perfectly competitive."[5]

The economy has been geared to a stable, virtually stationary, routine pattern. Not that the Indian is not always looking for new ways to improve his lot. Tax notes that "he is on the lookout for new and better seeds, fertilizer, ways of planting." But such improvements come along infrequently, and their effects upon production are exceedingly small. There was a growing demand by "foreigners" for some shore land along Lake Atitlan but this development was having very little effect upon the land Indians used for producing crops and on which they built their huts. Some buses and trucks had become available for transport to more distant towns and they were being used to go to and from markets in these towns because it was "cheaper" than walking and carrying the goods. There were more tourists in and about the lake but these too were having little or no discernible influence on the community.[6]

All the evidence revealed in the careful documentation of the behavior of the people in *Penny Capitalism* and in the many tables showing prices, costs, and returns strongly supports the inference that the people are remarkably efficient in allocating the factors at their disposal in current production. There are no significant indivisibilities in methods of production, none in factors, and none in products. There is no disguised unemployment, no underemployment of either men, women, or children old enough to work, and

5. Ibid., p. 13. Italics are from Tax.

6. Professor Tax had occasion to revisit this Indian community in Guatemala after a lapse of 20 years. The overwhelming impression of the brief visit was that life and the economy had remained virtually unchanged.

for the least of them there is no such thing as a zero marginal product. Because even very young children can contribute something of value by working in the field, they cannot be spared the time to go to school. Product and factor prices are flexible. People respond to profit. For them every penny counts.

SENAPUR, INDIA: POOR BUT EFFICIENT

A study by W. David Hopper, "The Economic Organization of a Village in North Central India,"[7] portrays an economy in another part of the world performing as if it too were highly efficient in using the factors at hand. Hopper, like Tax, entered upon his study of this village as an anthropologist. Like Tax, after having lived in the community for a period and having observed its cultural, social, and other characteristics, he decided to concentrate heavily on the economy of the village.

For students of anthropology, there are undoubtedly important cultural and social differences between Senapur, India, and Panajachel, Guatemala.[8] There are also some

7. An unpublished Ph.D. thesis presented at Cornell University, June 1957. The village of Senapur is located on the Ganges Plain. At the time of the study, it comprised 1,046 acres and had a population of about 2,100. Hopper resided in Senapur from October 1953 to February 1955.

8. Senapur, for instance, has a long-established caste system, whereas the Guatemalan community has singular flexibility in the movement of families up and down its social status scale. In Senapur the families of the privileged castes, mainly the Thakur, have perpetuated their wealth, privileges, and social status for many generations. In the Guatemalan community, Tax found marriages cutting across wealth lines and much mobility on the economic and social scale; moreover, the social and economic gap separating the top and the other families has not been substantial. Thus even the varying winds of fortune make for much mobility from one generation to the next as one sees these families in *Penny Capitalism.*

differences in the level of production and consumption. Senapur is not as poor as Panajachel, but by Western standards it is nevertheless poor. Senapur has a school with grades 1 to 5 which until very recently served mainly the more privileged castes. The number of "productive" animals is unbelievably large: 270 milch cows and buffaloes; 480 bullocks to work in the fields. The stock of capital includes irrigation wells, ditches, storage ponds, digging tools, plows, chaff-cutters, and some small equipment. There is more specialization in Senapur than in the Guatemalan community: well-diggers, potters, carpenters, brick-makers, a blacksmith, and others. But for all that Senapur is poor.

Hopper examines with care the factors of production over which the people of Senapur have command. There is a fine set of natural resources characteristic of that part of India, and there is a substantial set of reproducible resources both within this community and outside that also serves its production and consumption activities. He then traces the behavior of the competitive forces as these are revealed through the established product and factor markets.

Hopper summarizes an important part of this study thusly: "An observer in Senapur cannot help but be impressed with the way the village uses its physical resources. The age-old techniques have been refined and sharpened by countless years of experience, and each generation seems to have had its experimenters who added a bit here and changed a practice there, and thus improved the community lore. Rotations, tillage and cultivation practices, seed rates, irrigation techniques, and the ability of the blacksmith and potter to work under handicaps of little power and inferior materials, all attest to a cultural heritage that is richly endowed with empirical wisdom." Hopper then puts this question to himself: "Are the people of Senapur realizing the full economic potential of their physical resources? . . . From the point of view of the villagers the answer must be 'Yes' for in general each man comes close to doing the best that he can with his knowledge and cultural background."[9]

Fortunately, the data that Hopper collected have permitted him to make a rigorous test of the allocative hypothesis under consideration.[10] He made such a test by determining the set of relative prices of products and factors implicit in the allocation decisions revealed in the data. In determining the allocative efficiency of the farmers from the prices implicit in their production activities, Hopper used the price of barley as the numeraire. The implicit prices in terms of barley for each product estimated from factor allocations, with barley at 1.00, are wheat, 1.325; pea, .943; and gram, .828. The implicit price estimates for each factor based on its production use at the average product prices and their standard errors are as follows.[11]

	Barley	*Wheat*	*Pea*	*Gram*	*Average*
Average Price	1.00	1.325	.943	.828	
Price of:	Used in Production of:				
Land (acres)	4.416 (1.056)	4.029 (.855)	4.405 (1.185)	4.845 (.857)	4.424
Bullock time (hours)	.0696 (.0116)	.0716 (.0098)	.0820 (.0180)	.0834 (.0156)	.0774
Labour (hours)	.0086 (.0026)	.0097 (.0037)	.0087 (.0021)	.0076 (.0030)	.0086
Irrigation Water (750 gals.)	.0355 (.0122)	.0326 (.0078)	.0305 (.0111)	.0315 (.0234)	.0325

9. Hopper, p. 161.

10. W. David Hopper, "Resource Allocation on a Sample of Indian Farms," University of Chicago, Office of Agricultural Economics Research, Paper No. 6104 (April 21, 1961, mimeo.).

11. W. David Hopper, "Allocation Efficiency in Traditional Indian Agriculture," *Journal of Farm Economics* (forthcoming).

From these data and his test, Hopper infers that "there is a remarkably close correspondence between the various price estimates. It would appear that the average allocations made by the sample of farms were efficient within the context of the prevailing technical relationships. There is no evidence that an improvement in economic output could be obtained by altering the present allocations as long as the village relies on traditional resources and technology."

The implicit prices also match closely the market prices of products and factors for which there were market prices. These prices follow:

Product or factor	*Relative barley price*	*Adjusted to the barley price (in rupees)*	*Actual market price (in rupees)*
Barley (md.)	1.00	9.85	9.85
Wheat (md.)	1.325	13.05	14.20
Pea (md.)	.943	9.29	10.40
Gram (md.)	.828	8.16	10.85
Land (acres)	4.424	43.57	8.00 to 30.00 (cash rent only)
Bullock time (hrs.)	.0774	.762	not available
Labor (hrs.)	.0086	.085	.068 (cash and kind only)
Irrigation water (750 gals.)	.0325	.321	not available

The implicit prices of these products, except for gram, match closely the actual market prices. Hopper observes that in the case of gram there is a lagged response under way to a strengthening market for gram; the relative price of gram had been rising for three years prior to the date of Hopper's study. The findings in this important study show that there is a "close approximation between market and implicit prices." The factors of production available to the people of Senapur were allocated efficiently, and the test therefore strongly supports the hypothesis here proposed.

INFERENCES AND IMPLICATIONS

The data pertaining to the allocation of factors for current production in Panajachel and Senapur are consistent with the hypothesis proposed at the outset of this chapter. It is important to note, however, in drawing the inference that there are no significant inefficiencies in the allocation of factors in these two communities, that the concept of factors includes more than land, labor, and capital as these are commonly defined. It also includes the state of the arts, or the techniques of production, that are an integral part of the material capital, skills, and technical knowledge of a people. In other words, factors are not treated by abstracting from the state of the arts. By this all-inclusive concept of factors, the community is poor because the factors on which the economy is dependent are not capable of producing more under existing circumstances. Conversely, under these simplified conditions, the observed poverty is not a consequence of any significant inefficiencies in factor allocation.

Although it is not feasible to show that these two communities are typical of a large class of poor agricultural communities, the assumption that they are seems highly plausible. Moreover, this plausibility is supported by the fact that the hypothesis under consideration appears to be consistent with a wide array of other empirical studies of such communities. The well-known studies of the farm economy of China by

Buck[12] lend support as do the many examples cited by Bauer and Yamey.[13] A comprehensive examination of all such data is, however, beyond the scope of this study.

The economic premises on which the hypothesis rests, and the support it receives empirically, warrant treating it as a proposition likely to be widely useful. As such, it has a number of implications, some already mentioned.

What does illiteracy imply? The fact that people are illiterate does not mean that they are therefore insensitive to the standards set by marginal costs and returns in allocating the factors they have at their disposal. What it does indicate is that the human agent has fewer capabilities than he would have if he had acquired the skills and useful knowledge associated with schooling. Although schooling may increase greatly the productivity of the human agent, it is not a prerequisite to an efficient allocation of the existing stock of factors. The notion that these poor agricultural communities do not have enough competent entrepreneurs to do a satisfactory job in using the factors at hand is in all probability mistaken. In some cases these entrepreneurs may be subject to political or social restraints that give rise to allocative inefficiencies, but the adverse production effects of such restraints are quite another matter.

There is another inference that is contrary to a widely held view, namely that farmers in these communities do not respond to developments that alter the stock of factors at their disposal. This view holds that the farmers do not adjust to changes in relative prices of products and factors.

12. John Lossing Buck, *Chinese Farm Economy* (Chicago, University of Chicago Press, 1930).

13. Peter T. Bauer and Basil S. Yamey, *The Economics of Under-Developed Countries,* a Cambridge Economic Handbook (Chicago, University of Chicago Press, 1957), Ch. VI.

If this is true, it is inconceivable that the community could ever become essentially efficient in factor allocation, except by sheer accident. Both Hopper and Tax, however, are explicit in noting that these farmers do respond. The question may be formulated thusly: if an irrigation canal is constructed or a new and better variety of a particular crop becomes available, do they respond? A pioneering study by Raj Krishna[14] of the supply responses of farmers in the Punjab during the twenties and thirties indicates that the lag in adjustment in producing cotton was about the same as it has been for cotton farmers in the United States. Quite aside from the rate at which they adjust to alterations in economic conditions, however, the important fact at this juncture of the analysis is that they do respond. It therefore follows that whenever such a community has for decades been living a quiet, routine economic life it has long since achieved an essentially efficient allocation of factors at its disposal.

There is one set of estimates based on cross-sectional Cobb-Douglas type production functions which includes six classes of farms in India that appear to show extraordinary inefficiencies in factor allocations. Heady includes these six Indian sets in a list of 32 that covers locations in various parts of the world.[15] The six sets covering farms in India are based presumably on data for the middle 1950s. In these the marginal returns to labor range from .03 to 1.78 for each

14. Raj Krishna, "Farm Supply Response in the Punjab (India-Pakistan): A Case Study of Cotton," (unpublished Ph.D. dissertation, University of Chicago, 1961).

15. Earl O. Heady, "Techniques of Production, Size of Productive Units, and Factor Supply Conditions," Paper presented at the Social Science Research Council Conference on Relations between Agriculture and Economic Growth, Stanford University, Stanford, California, November 11–12, 1960.

1.00 (unit) of labor costs.[16] For land, the range of the marginal returns to costs is even wider, with the lowest at .05 and the highest at 3.60 for 1.00 (unit) of land rental. The most extreme results, however, are those reported for reproducible material capital. For these the marginal returns range from –.85 to 6.97 per 1.00 (unit) of capital costs.

Although Heady mentions the possible limitations that qualify the usefulness of these estimates,[17] they are nevertheless treated as if they could be taken seriously. Hopper's careful examination of the data problem in Senapur, India, makes it abundantly clear that such "monthly wage rates" and "rental returns" to land are most inaccurate. In the case of capital, Heady reveals that the "selection of interest rate for capital is itself a problem,"[18] because it ranges "from 6 to 200 percent." It is no wonder that the results of working with such data are so meaningless. If these agricultural communities in India had been experiencing rapid economic development and were therefore confronted by large changes in factor and product prices to which they had not as yet had time enough to adjust, there would be a logical basis for some inequalities in marginal returns relative to the costs of factors. But no such major developments had taken place in India at that time. It is noteworthy that no logical explanation of the extreme ranges in the estimates cited for

16. In the case of labor, no estimate is shown for wheat farming in Uttar Pradesh, India, undoubtedly the most absurd of the lot, for it is this set that shows a marginal return to land of 2.22 and to capital of 6.97 for each unit (1.00) of input costs.

17. Among these possible limitations, Heady lists "(a) specification bias, (b) aggregation, (c) algebraic form, (d) sampling, and (e) other facets of statistical inference. However, we believe that the data do, even though they represent a small stratum of national agriculture, provide some qualitative types comparisons." P. 35.

18. Heady, "Techniques of Production," p. 35.

the six sets of farming in India is offered. Had one been attempted, the untenable nature of the results would have become apparent.

Still another implication stemming from the proposition that a large class of poor agricultural communities shows comparatively few significant inefficiencies in factor allocation is that competent farm managers, whether national or foreign, cannot show the farmers how to allocate better the existing factors of production. Once again it must be stressed that this implication holds provided these competent experts are restricted in advising farmers to the existing factors, which means that they do not alter the opportunity to increase production by introducing other factors, including knowledge about the availability of such other factors.

Lastly, then, there is the implication that no part of the labor force working in agriculture in these communities has a marginal productivity of zero. But since this particular implication runs counter to a well-established doctrine, the next chapter is devoted to an examination of the basis of this doctrine and the reasons why it is a misleading conception of the economics of labor productivity in poor agricultural communities.

4 THE DOCTRINE OF AGRICULTURAL LABOR OF ZERO VALUE

The concept underlying the doctrine of labor of zero value is one of workers in agriculture who contribute nothing to production. However much they work during the year,[1] according to this concept, they add nothing to what

Zvi Griliches, Dale W. Jorgenson, and Anthony M. Tang were especially helpful in their criticisms of an early draft of this chapter.

Since the chapter was completed, the unpublished Ph.D. dissertation of Berdj Kenadjian, "Disguised Unemployment in Underdeveloped Countries" (Harvard University, 1957), has been called to the attention of the writer by Professor Frank Fetter of Northwestern University. It is a careful and critical study of the theoretical presuppositions of those who have promulgated the concept of "disguised unemployment" and an exhaustive examination of the empirical data used by those who have tried to support the concept with "estimates." Anyone who wishes to pursue the matter further will be well advised to turn to the study by Kenadjian, including the very useful bibliography of the relevant literature.

1. Some writers have let the seasonality of agricultural work confuse them. It is quite untidy analytically to mix the two concepts. Agricul-

is produced. The marginal productivity of this labor is zero. Therefore, without changing anything else of consequence, a removal of this part of the labor force from agriculture will not reduce production. It follows that this part of the agricultural labor force is wholly redundant; it is surplus labor, and is available for industrialization at no (opportunity) costs except the costs of transfer.

The concept does not rest on differences in the capabilities of workers. It is therefore not like the concept of "no-rent" land used to differentiate among some parcels of land. There are of course some persons who are either too old or too young, or who are debilitated and too weak to do any useful work. These are not the people who enter into this concept of labor. *The concept pertains only to those persons who want to work, who are capable of working, and who are in fact working.* Nor does the concept imply that the redundant labor is without any personal income. Such income, however, must come either from other factors belonging to such workers or from transfers within the family or among families in the community.

Those who have promulgated the concept have held that it applies predominantly to agriculture in low income countries. How much of the agricultural labor force in these countries is in the "zero value" class? The figure 25 per cent appears again and again.[2] If this is correct, a quarter of the

---

tural work may be concentrated in a short period, e.g. in wheat growing, and yet the (annual) productivity of this labor may be as large as that of labor in other types of farming that require many more days of work a year.

2. P. N. Rosenstein-Rodan writing in 1943 simply assumed "that about 25% of the population is either totally or partially . . . unemployed," in Eastern and Southeastern Europe (*Economic Journal, 53*). W. Arthur Lewis in 1955 states that "Detailed calculations for India . . . have led

agricultural labor force is "free labor" in the sense that it is available for other purposes, i.e. for industrialization, at no cost except that of transfer. Thus a doctrine is born.

The trouble with this doctrine is that it rests on a shaky conception of labor productivity in agriculture and is not consistent with any relevant data. Attempts have been made to give it a theoretical base by treating agriculture as if it were subject to particular technical restraints; but, as will be shown later, these restraints are so farfetched that they hardly warrant critical examination. The analysis set forth by Leibenstein, based on a redistribution of the existing supply of food among fewer agricultural workers to show that under particular circumstances the total effective brute force of the remaining labor force could be increased, while an important issue, is, as Leibenstein makes clear, quite another matter.[3]

Three aspects of the doctrine are considered briefly in what follows: (1) its roots; (2) an attempt to give it a theoretical base; and (3) some empirical data bearing on the matter. Before turning to these, there are two crucial characteristics of agriculture in poor communities that require a preliminary comment: the productivity of labor is in gen-

---

to the conclusion that at least a quarter of the agricultural population is surplus to requirements." (*The Theory of Economic Growth* [London, Allen & Unwin, 1955], p 327.)

3. Harvey Leibenstein, *Economic Backwardness and Economic Growth* (New York, Wiley, 1957); Leibenstein, "The Theory of Underemployment in Backward Economies," *Journal of Political Economy, 65* (April 1957); Leibenstein, "Underemployment in Backward Economies, Some Additional Notes," *Journal of Political Economy, 66* (June 1958); and Jacob Viner, "Some Reflections on the Concept of 'Disguised Unemployment,'" *Contribuicoes a Analise do Desenvolvimento Economico* (Rio de Janeiro, Livraria Agir Editora, 1957).

eral very low; and agricultural production as a rule diminishes when some appreciable part of the labor force is withdrawn provided that nothing else of consequence is changed.

It is easy to see why the first of these readily misleads the casual observer who is accustomed to measuring margins in dollars. For him the difference between the penny-like margin and zero is at best difficult to discern. He is not likely to see margins that are worth only a penny, though these margins are real and relevant in such an economy. The second characteristic is in substance the evidence for the inference here advanced, namely, that agricultural labor of zero value consistent with the concept under scrutiny does not exist.

It will help clarify matters to distinguish among the following three economic states:

1. One in which the marginal product of labor in agriculture is very low because of the factors at the disposal of the community, and in which labor in agriculture produces as much as does comparable labor in other sectors when costs of transfers are properly reckoned. Such is the state of penny capitalism of Panajachel, Guatemala, already discussed.

2. Another in which the marginal product of labor in agriculture is less than that of comparable labor in other sectors of the economy after the costs of transfer are taken into account. This state is the type of disequilibrium that characterizes much of modern agriculture; although adjustments are being made, there is nevertheless an excess supply of labor in agriculture.

3. Still another state, in which the marginal productivity of part of the labor working in agriculture is zero.

The first and second economic states are fundamental in understanding agriculture. The first, as already indicated, is typical of many poor agricultural communities because they are in a stable state of long-run equilibrium. The second is related predominantly to growth and to lags in adjustment, and it represents one of the disequilibria that is rooted in economic growth. It can persist for decades, and is presently most evident in some of the countries in which agriculture is technically in the vanguard. There are many subtypes of disequilibria between those characterizing poor agricultural communities that have just begun to modernize and those that are farthest advanced in this respect. It is, however, the third of these economic states that is under consideration here. Although the concept of "labor of zero value" is sometimes also applied to the effects of new and better agricultural factors of production upon the marginal product of labor in agriculture, it will here be restricted to the effects upon production of the withdrawal of labor without changing the techniques of production or the amounts and forms of nonhuman and human capital.

A NETWORK OF ROOTS

The roots of this doctrine tell a lot about its popularity and persuasiveness. The failure of the aggregate demand of Western industrial countries to support full employment, which was patently true during the long and deep depression of the thirties, obviously affected many poor agrarian countries adversely. But since these poor countries were predominantly agricultural, they did not experience the visible forms of mass unemployment.[4] People simply

4. The "underemployment" in modern agriculture characteristic of the second of the three economic states presented above is a concept

continued to work at farming, and this gave rise to the presumption that many of them must be producing nothing of value. The industrial mass unemployment observed at home, so it is believed, had its counterpart in labor of zero value working in agriculture abroad. The belief that a part of employed labor in agriculture has a marginal productivity of zero persists despite the post-World War II recovery and the large upsurge in national production. Meanwhile, the factual basis of this simple view has been shaken by the many experiments in increasing the money supply in poor countries to induce increases in production by drawing the "zero value" agricultural workers into production, which have resulted only in inflation.[5]

The tap root of this doctrine has been a set of bad statistical estimates that emerged from playing the game of treating agricultural production as if it could be organized to employ all agricultural workers ten hours a day the year round (Sundays and holidays off, of course), or of taking the combination of factors of production and the higher labor outputs that had been achieved in a technically more advanced country and applying this mix of factors to the poor agricultural country. The players of this game failed to understand the most elementary basis of the seasonality of agriculture; they also failed to realize that the absolute decline in the size of the labor force in agriculture in a few high income countries is a very recent development and has been

---

the writer used extensively in *Agriculture in an Unstable Economy* (New York, McGraw-Hill, 1945), esp. pp. 47 and 189–201. This concept has also been applied to traditional agriculture where it is not applicable.

5. Theodore W. Schultz, *The Economic Test in Latin America,* New York State School of Industrial and Labor Relations Bulletin 35 (Ithaca, Cornell University, August 1956), pp. 14–15.

made possible by the introduction into agriculture of truly modern factors that are substitutes for farm labor and also for land.

Still another root supporting the doctrine has been the pronouncements of the agricultural expert who goes abroad. The expert carries with him an image of excess labor in agriculture, which has been the state of agriculture for some time in Western countries, notably the United States. What the expert sees in agriculture abroad is affected by his image of the disequilibrium that characterizes so much of modern agriculture. He sees therefore many workers in agriculture producing unbelievably little when they work, and many of them appear to be idle much of the time. The belief that he is seeing even more excess labor in agriculture than he knows exists, for example, in the United States is highly plausible to him. The economist ought to have been on his guard, however, in accepting this view of the agricultural technician because of the other pronouncements he makes. The agricultural expert does not single out labor, as is the wont of some economists, as the only factor that is "underutilized" in poor agricultural communities. He is a technician who sees the state of agriculture as "inefficient" in all manner of things. He is quick to point out that land is poorly "utilized," and so are irrigation facilities. Too little fertilizer is applied, and what is used is not the optimum mixture of soil nutrients. Seeds, grain storage facilities, draft animals, and equipment—all elicit the same judgment. There should be no mistake on the point that the agricultural technician is not asking what the agricultural community can produce with the precise factors at its disposal; he is concerned about the fundamental problem of modernizing agriculture, which is a wholly different matter.

A BOW TO THEORY

What is the theoretical basis for the concept that the marginal productivity of part of the labor force working in agriculture is zero? Eckaus introduces two conditions, namely, "factor-market imperfections" and "limited technical substitutability of factors."[6] The array of factor-market imperfections examined by Eckaus are not essential to his argument nor are they specific to the economy of a poor country. His case for labor of zero value in agriculture rests squarely on the assumption that there is no opportunity for technical substitution of factors in agriculture at any of the relevant margins. But this critical assumption is surely contrary to fact, for nowhere can one observe the necessary significant indivisibilities either in products, factors, or methods of production in agriculture that would support the assumption. The perceptions of Viner are true and clear: "I find it impossible to conceive of a farm of any kind on which, other factors of production being held constant in quantity, and even in form as well, it would not be possible, by known methods, to obtain some addition to the crop by using additional labor in more careful selection and planting of the seed, more intensive weeding, cultivation, thinning, and mulching, more painstaking harvesting, gleaning, and cleaning of the crop."[7]

Although the theoretical basis of this doctrine is shaky, the belief persists that a removal of 25 per cent of the labor on the land in poor countries will not reduce agricultural production.[8]

6. R. S. Eckaus, "Factor Proportions in Underdeveloped Countries," *American Economic Review, 45* (September 1955).

7. Viner, "Some Reflections," p. 347.

8. Nasir Ahmad Khan, *Problems of Growth of an Underdeveloped Economy* (Bombay, Asia Publishing House, 1961).

EMPIRICAL TEST

A theory may appear to rest on assumptions that are farfetched, and yet it may prove useful in explaining particular data. Thus the question is: are there data which behave as if a part of the labor force in agriculture has a marginal productivity of zero? Suppose there were a poor agricultural community from which 25 per cent, or less, of the labor force had been induced to leave and in which nothing else of consequence had been altered, and suppose agricultural production were to remain about constant. Such data would conform to the theory.

To observe that all of the labor force in agriculture work part of the time, and most of them much of the time, does not in itself contradict the theory. It is not a theory pertaining to seasonal unemployment, as noted earlier. The many records cited by Oshima[9] and Buck[10] of labor shortages during harvest and other peak work periods in agriculture in poor communities are not a clear test, because they do not show whether the marginal productivity of a part of this labor is or is not zero.

The increases in agricultural production that have occurred while the labor force in agriculture has declined during recent decades in some countries is obviously not a test of the theory because of the modernization and additional capital underlying these developments. Nor are changes in agricultural production that occur during a major war a

9. Harry T. Oshima, "Underemployment in Backward Economies: An Empirical Comment," *Journal of Political Economy, 66* (June 1958).
10. John Lossing Buck, *Land Utilization in China* (Chicago, University of Chicago Press, 1937), Vol. 1.

satisfactory test because of other large disturbances such a war imposes upon an economy.[11]

The cases where the demand for additional nonfarm labor rises sharply and where workers leave nearby farms are relevant provided the change occurs quickly so that there has not been enough time to substitute additional capital for the farm labor withdrawn. There are many such cases no doubt but dependable data are hard to come by. "Reports" on such matters that an observer obtains may be true but they lack the magic of published statistics. Two such cases were described by this writer on another occasion.[12] In Peru a road was constructed down the east slope of the Andes to Tingo Maria. To build this road some labor was drawn from farms adjacent to the road, mostly within walking distances. Agricultural production, it was reported, dropped promptly. In Bel Horizonte, Brazil, an upsurge in construction in the city drew workers to it from the nearby countryside, and here too the reports were that agricultural production fell as a consequence.

It would seem that famines and resulting deaths might provide the necessary test. But it turns out that the effects upon production of such deaths among the agricultural labor force are hard to assess, because they are confounded by the

11. P. N. Rosenstein-Rodan, "Disguised Unemployment and Underemployment in Agriculture," *Monthly Bulletin of Agricultural Economics and Statistics, 6* (Rome, July–August 1957), 5–6. He claims that the agricultural output in German-occupied Poland during the Second World War did not decrease after about 20 per cent of its agricultural population was removed. One wishes he had given the sources of the data on which this claim rests. But even so it would not be a test because of compulsions and the catastrophic disturbances wrought on Poland by the war.

12. Theodore W. Schultz, "The Role of Government in Promoting Economic Growth," in *The State of the Social Sciences,* ed. Leonard D. White (Chicago, University of Chicago Press, 1956), p. 375.

debilitating effects a famine has upon the workers who survive. The influenza epidemic of 1918–19, however, should make it possible to test the hypothesis that the marginal product of a part of the labor force in agriculture in poor countries is zero. The epidemic struck suddenly. Deaths reached a peak within weeks and then the toll as a rule receded rapidly. The epidemic did not leave long debilitated those who survived. There were at least two countries, India and Mexico, in which the epidemic of 1918–19 took a tremendous toll of lives. Both of these countries consisted predominantly of poor agricultural communities, which were hard hit. Such signs as are available on what happened in Mexico indicate strongly that the population in a number of states declined significantly, and that agricultural production fell as a consequence. Yet one cannot be sure because the data are sketchy and because of the agrarian reforms being promulgated at that time. In India, however, there were no reforms to complicate matters.

THE TEST IN INDIA FOLLOWING THE 1918–19 INFLUENZA EPIDEMIC

Did India maintain its agricultural production following the heavy losses of rural manpower of 1918–19? If it did, this would be consistent with the hypothesis that a part of the agricultural labor force had been redundant. The available data, although fragmentary on some matters, do permit what appears to be a decisive answer to this question.

The following relevant circumstances should be borne in mind. The preceding crop year, 1917–18, was one of the best that British India (now India and Pakistan) had enjoyed in years. Thus, when the epidemic struck, food was ample by

Indian standards because crops had been good. The influenza epidemic did not affect animals and therefore did not decrease any of the factors of production except the number of workers. This means that land, irrigation facilities, and draft animals were not impaired. The people who succumbed were not sick long and survivors recovered quickly. Thus the population that survived, unlike what happens following a severe famine, was not long debilitated.[13]

According to the monumental study of Kingsley Davis, the influenza epidemic of 1918–19 killed about 20 million people in India,[14] which is equal to about 6 per cent of the 1918 population.[15] The death rate among the active labor force in agriculture was substantially higher than for the population as a whole.[16] Within India, the western and

13. The writer is indebted to Dr. Phillip Miller of the faculty of the School of Medicine of the University of Chicago for guidance into some of the relevant medical literature and for judgments on the normal course that illness took.

14. Kingsley Davis, *The Population of India and Pakistan* (Princeton, Princeton University Press, 1951). Davis's estimates come to 18.5 million deaths attributed to the epidemic. A check of the method indicates that this estimate is on the low side. He closes Appendix B with a statement that 20 million deaths is as satisfactory an estimate as can be made.

15. Davis places the 1918 population at 322 million. Thus deaths were 6.2 per cent of that figure.

16. S. P. James, *Report on the Pandemic of Influenza, 1918–19,* Reports on Public Health and Medical Subjects, Report Number 4 (Great Britain, Ministry of Health, 1920), Pt. II, Ch. 2. James states (p. 384) that in India the mortality rate in rural areas during the virulent epidemic of September–December 1918 "far exceeded that of the towns." The number of deaths attributed to the epidemic was high in the ages 20 to 45 relative to the rest of the population. Table 9 of Davis's study shows that the infant mortality rate was 30 per cent higher in 1918 than in 1917, whereas the death rate of the entire population rose to more than twice the normal rate in India. A study of 1918–19 influenza deaths in a part of the United States shows the toll to have been relatively high in the ages 20–45 also, and that deaths per thousand among poor people, noticeably among American Indians, were four times as large as in the

northern parts suffered a much higher death rate than the eastern parts.[17] In some of the eastern parts, it appears that the influenza death rate was about 2 per cent while in those parts where the influenza was most virulent the death rate was 15 per cent and higher.

Inasmuch as agriculture in India is highly sensitive to changes in weather (rainfall), the 1916–17 crop year will be taken as the base year instead of 1917–18. The latter, as already noted, was a bumper crop year. The crop year 1916–17, on the other hand, while a good year was in general comparable in this respect to 1919–20, the first full year following the influenza epidemic. Rainfall appears to have been moderately better than normal for India during both of these crop years. The official agricultural statistics of British India were predominantly concerned about the land area devoted to crops and not about yield. The area sown to crops, including double cropping (counting the area twice), is the best available proxy for agricultural production. It should be noted, however, that where there are many people relative to land and much land is cultivated intensively the expectation is that acreage sown is less sensitive to a decrease in the labor force than total yield.[18] Accordingly, if acreage

---

larger cities. See Edwin O. Jordan, *Epidemic Influenza* (Chicago, American Medical Association, 1927), and Pt. I of the report in which James's contribution appears.

17. James, *Report,* p. 384.

18. The acreage sown would be less sensitive than total yield on the assumption that as a consequence of the reduction in the labor force there were not only fewer acres cropped twice a year and some land left idle that had become sub-marginal because of a rise in the value of labor, but also the acreage sown to crops would have been cultivated less intensively than formerly and this would have reduced the yield on the acreage sown. Another interpretation of the decrease in acreage sown would be that the attrition in the labor force occurred in such a way that it would have been impossible by 1919–20 to have reallocated

sown decreased in response to the deaths in labor force caused by the influenza epidemic, it would be a more decisive test than would a reduction of the same percentage in agricultural production.

Before turning to the data, it will be helpful in interpreting the relationships to keep two alternative hypotheses in mind: (1) the deaths had no effect on agricultural production, assuming that the part of the agricultural labor force with a marginal productivity of zero was at least as large as the number of agricultural workers who died; (2) the coefficient of labor in agricultural production in India was in the neighborhood of .4 and the elasticity of output with respect to labor was such that a 10 per cent decrease in labor, holding all other inputs constant, would have resulted in a 4 per cent reduction in agricultural output.[19]

The agricultural labor force in India may have been reduced by about 8 per cent as a consequence of the 1918–19 epidemic.[20] The area sown to crops was reduced sharply the year of the influenza, falling from 265 million in 1916–17 to 228 million in 1918–19. This drop, however, is confounded by some adverse weather and by the many millions of people

---

the remaining labor force efficiently. For this interpretation, the extreme assumption would be that in some villages all of the relevant labor force died while in other (distant) villages none died from influenza and for the remaining labor to become reallocated would require a number of years. There is, however, no plausible evidence to my knowledge that would support this interpretation.

19. There are some sample surveys covering parts of agriculture in India during some more recent years that provide the basis for this hypothesis.

20. The death rate for all British India of 6.2 per cent (Davis, *Population of India and Pakistan,* Appendix B) for reasons already indicated fell heavily on the agricultural labor force between the ages of 20 and 45 in rural areas. On the assumption that this exceeded the average death rate by one-third, a death rate of 8.3 is indicated.

who became ill and who were therefore incapacitated for a part of the crop year. For reasons already presented, 1919–20 is the appropriate year to use in this analysis. The area sown in 1919–20 was, however, 10 million acres below, or 3.8 per cent less than that of the base year 1916–17. In general, the provinces of India with the highest death rates attributed to the epidemic also had the largest percentage declines in acreage sown to crops. It would be hard to find any support in these data for the doctrine that a part of the labor force in agriculture in India at the time of the epidemic had a marginal productivity of zero.

As has been mentioned, a few fairly recent sample surveys, indicate that the coefficient of labor in agricultural production in India may be about .4. A hypothesis based on the assumption that this estimate may be generally applicable is supported surprisingly well by the data appearing in Tables 1 and 2. For all British India, it predicts a decrease in agricultural production of 3.3 per cent and the observed reduction in acreage sown is 3.8 per cent. The eastern provinces of India had a relatively small death toll from the 1918–19 influenza epidemic, and the reductions in acreage sown were correspondingly small. In Burma the growth trend prevailed. Among the western and northern provinces, where the death rate was exceedingly high, the declines in acreage sown were correspondingly large.[21]

To determine the statistical significance, a direct approach[22] is to estimate the labor coefficient from the data

21. Bombay province is most out of line in that the observed decrease in acreage sown is not as large as predicted. The reason is clearly that the rainfall in Bombay during 1919–20 was substantially above normal.

22. This approach was suggested by Dale W. Jorgenson. It is of interest to note that the estimate of the labor coefficient (.349) is virtually the same as that shown for the Punjab in Table 3 of the *Note on Factor Shares.*

and to test the hypothesis that this coefficient is equal to .4. This approach gives the following estimates:

labor coefficient = .349
standard error of the labor coefficient = .076

TABLE 1

Changes in Acreage Sown to Crops, and the Observed and Predicted Agricultural Production Effects of 1918–19 Influenza Epidemic, India and Major Provinces of India

Province and all India	*Acreage sown to crops in millions*[a]		*Observed and predicted change (1916–17 = 100)*	
	1916–17	*1919–20*	*Observed*	*Predicted*[b]
(1)	(2)	(3)	(4)	(5)
Central Province and Berar	27.9	25.9	93.0	91.7
Bombay	28.3	27.7	97.9	93.1
Punjab	31.7	29.1	91.8	94.3
North West Frontier Province	2.87	2.67	93.0	94.5
United Province	46.6	43.5	93.4	94.6
Bihar-Orissa	31.8	31.9	100.5	97.4
Assam	6.4	6.2	96.4	97.7
Madras	39.0	38.2	97.8	97.9
Burma	15.2	15.8	104.0	98.3
Bengal	29.2	28.8	98.6	98.9
All British India	265.0	255.0	96.2	96.7

Sarma Mallampally assisted in checking the underlying data and the calculations that appear in Tables 1 and 2. He found the estimates by J. T. Marten (see Table 2, n. a) which were better than those by S. P. James, *Report on the Pandemic of Influenza, 1918–19,* which I had drawn upon, although the two sets are in general consistent.

a. India, Department of Statistics, *Agricultural Statistics of India, 37th Issue, 1920–21,* Vol. 1 (Calcutta, Supt. of Government Printing, India, 1922).

b. Based on the hypothesis that the coefficient of labor in agricultural production was 0.4. See Table 2, Col. 4.

TABLE 2

Deaths Attributed to Influenza Epidemic of 1918–19, and Predicted and Observed Effects on Agricultural Production for India and Major Provinces of India

Province and all India (1)	A measure of the distribution of deaths (per 100 population)[a] (2)	Adjusted distribution of deaths (per 100 population)[b] (3)	Predicted reduction in agricultural production (in per cent)[d] (4)	Observed reduction in acreage sown to crops (in per cent)[e] (5)
Central Province and Berar	6.64	15.60	8.32	7.00
Bombay	5.49	12.90	6.88	2.10
Punjab	4.54	10.67	5.69	8.20
North West Frontier Province	4.36	10.25	5.47	7.00
United Province	4.34	10.20	5.44	6.60
Bihar-Orissa	2.05	4.82	2.57	+0.50
Assam	1.86	4.37	2.33	3.60
Madras	1.67	3.92	2.09	2.20
Burma	1.39	3.27	1.74	+4.00
Bengal	0.85	2.00	1.07	1.40
All British India	2.64	6.20[c]	3.30	3.80

a. India, Census of India, 1921, Vol. 1, Part 1, Report by J. T. Marten, p. 13. Also see James, p. 384.

b. Kingsley Davis, *The Population of India and Pakistan* (Princeton, Princeton University Press, 1951). Appendix B places total deaths at 20 million. Col. 2 is multiplied by 2.35 to adjust census data to the Davis estimate.

c. Based on Davis, i.e., total population 322 million, deaths 20 million. The 2.64 appearing in Col. 2 is implicit, namely, 6.20 ·/· 2.35.

d. The death rate of the agricultural labor force was higher than that of the population as a whole. Various studies by the Office of U.S. Public Health indicate that deaths among males ages 10–59 were about one-third higher than that for the population as a whole. Accounts on India are consistent with this estimate. Accordingly Col. 3 is increased by one-third and then multiplied by 0.4, the coefficient of labor in agricultural production underlying the second hypothesis presented in the text.

e. Based on Col. 4 of Table 1.

Thus, using a confidence interval based on twice the standard error, the labor coefficient is .349 ± .152, and since this interval contains .4 the hypothesis that the labor coefficient is equal to .4 is accepted.

The conclusion with respect to the doctrine that a part of the labor working in agriculture in poor countries has a marginal productivity of zero is that it is a false doctrine. It has roots that make it suspect. It rests on shaky theoretical presumptions. It fails to win any support when put to a critical test in analyzing effects upon agricultural production of the deaths in the agricultural labor force caused by the influenza epidemic of 1918–19 in India.

5 IMPLICATIONS OF A THEORY OF THE PRICE OF INCOME STREAMS

The conception of traditional agriculture set forth in Chapter 2 is that of a particular type of economic equilibrium. The critical conditions that generate this type of equilibrium are as follows: (1) that the state of the arts remain constant, (2) that the state of preference and motives for holding and for acquiring sources of income remain constant, and (3) that both of these states remain constant long enough for marginal preferences and motives for holding and acquiring agricultural factors as sources of income to arrive at an equilibrium with the marginal productivity of these sources viewed as an investment in permanent income streams. The purpose of this chapter is to outline an approach for determining the price of these income streams and to examine its implications for economic growth from traditional agriculture.

In Chapter 3 it was convenient to leave the investment process aside while examining the efficiency with which the existing stock of agricultural factors, including human agents, are allocated in current production in traditional agriculture. To have abstracted from investment at that point could have had only a very small effect on the results because the total stock of reproducible factors can be increased only a little from one year to the next, even though net capital formation is large by normal standards relative to income. But in studying economic growth, whether from agriculture or from other sectors of an economy, investment is necessarily the core of the analysis.

In considering investment behavior, it is useful to distinguish between the investment response to inequalities in the marginal rates of return among agricultural factors and the investment response to differences in the general level of the rate of return. How large a source of growth are these inequalities? It is often said that in poor communities too much is invested in land and in precious trinkets relative to what is invested in agricultural structures, equipment, fertilizer, animals, seeds, and inventories. But when investment is restricted to traditional factors of production, the analysis underlying Chapter 3 raises serious doubts about the validity of the impressions on which such statements are based. One of the implications of the allocative efficiency already considered is that there are, as a rule, no significant inequalities in the rate of return to investment among the factors of production employed in traditional agriculture.

Suppose then that the marginal rates of return to all factors of production employed in traditional agriculture are approximately equal. What is the level of the rate of return?

The analytical task is to explain a low rate of net investment in traditional agriculture, or even no net investment whatsoever. There is general agreement that there are many poor agricultural communities like *Penny Capitalism* in which there is little or no net formation of reproducible material capital over time. But the explanations advanced for this investment behavior are far from satisfactory. They are based predominantly on the belief that these people generally have a low propensity to save despite a shortage of capital, or that these communities lack entrepreneurs who are sensitive to investment opportunities, or that savings and investment are not integrated to provide capital to take advantage of the investment opportunities that exist. All of these explanations rest on the presumption that the rate of return to such investments is in general high.

But if the rate of return to investment in traditional agriculture were low, real light would be cast on the matter. In that case, the implication would be that net investment had become small, or had even ceased, because of the weak incentive to save and invest. Then there would be straightaway an admissible economic reason for the observed investment behavior. A low rate of return would provide a logical basis for a low ratio of savings to income, for little or no foreign capital entering into traditional agriculture, and for a low rate of net capital formation. One of the purposes of this chapter is to present a theoretical basis for a low rate of return to investment in factors of production in traditional agriculture.

WHAT GROWTH MODELS OMIT

The literature pertaining to economic growth has for some time been dominated by particular macro-growth models, which abstract from changes over time in the relative prices of the factors of production and from changes in the profitability of investment related to these factor prices.[1] These particular models, therefore, are not designed to consider the effects of differences in the level of the rate of return to investment upon incentives to invest or upon growth. Yet it is obvious that the opportunity for growth, measured by the rate of return to investment, differs widely from sector to sector in an economy and also differs widely between countries and over time. But this critical variable is omitted from these particular macro-growth models.

There are several apparent reasons for this omission. The profitability of new classes of factors of production have been concealed under "technological change." Chapter 9 is devoted to this matter. Closely related is the failure to distinguish between traditional and modern factors of production and the differences between them in returns while the factors are being adopted and the economy adjusts to them. Although there has been a long-standing concern about the effects of the level of per family income upon the proportion of the income that is saved, there has been no comparable concern about the effects of differences in the relative price of new income streams upon savings and investment.

A THEORETICAL SCAFFOLD

The idea of economic growth denotes an increase in income. The economic growth revealed in national income accounts is based on measured (national) income.[2] Such

1. See F. A. Lutz and D. C. Hague, eds., *The Theory of Capital,* Proceedings of a Conference of the International Economic Association (London, Macmillan, 1961), Ch. I. See also E. Lundberg, "The Profitability of Investment," *Economic Journal, 69* (December 1959).

2. There are, of course, gains in welfare associated with economic growth that are not included in "measured national income." Decreases in the number of hours that people work per year or increases in the

growth from an agricultural sector means that there is an increase in income that has been made possible by agriculture. Income is a flow concept made up of income streams that are given quantitative dimensions per unit of time, e.g., a one-dollar-per-year income stream. Thus an increase in the number of income streams is equivalent to economic growth. Consequently, a growth rate of 3 per cent means that the number of income streams is increasing by 3 per cent per year.

To obtain an income stream it is essential to acquire the source of that stream. These sources are valuable, and each income stream has in this sense a price. A useful way of looking at economic growth is to identify the different sources of income streams and to determine the price at which each of the respective sources can be increased. The central economic problem then becomes one of explaining what determines the price of these income streams. In this approach it is meaningful to apply the concepts of demand and supply.

There are a number of advantages in focusing the analysis on income streams and applying the concepts of demand and supply in determining their price. It avoids the serious conceptual and logical difficulties inherent in aggregating capital and treating it as a stock. It also avoids the circularity of capitalizing the rent or return from capital by an interest rate to measure the stock of capital. It permits one to treat sources of income streams that are normally not bought and sold. Acquired skills of a labor force are important sources of income. In a society in which all men are free agents (none are slaves) there is no market in which such human capital is

amount of free time do not enter into the reckoning of measured national income, nor do all aspects of better schooling and improvements in health.

exchanged. Yet people invest in themselves and thus produce these means of production. There are also other important sources of income streams that are for all practical purposes on the same footing. There is in general no market in which experiment stations and other scientific research establishments, agricultural extension services, and schools are bought and sold. While it is conceivable that all of these could be placed under firms for profit, there are compelling economic reasons (to be elaborated later) for not doing so. Still another advantage arises out of the logical basis for distinguishing between the demanders and the suppliers of income streams, and the explanatory value of this distinction in understanding the fundamental role of each of them in economic growth.

It will simplify matters to abstract from the transitory income component and thus restrict the analysis to permanent income streams.[3] What will be the price of a permanent income stream? Suppose there is a market; the question can be approached in the same way as any other problem in price determination.[4] The pricing of these income streams is accordingly a consequence of the behavior of the respective demanders and suppliers. The demanders are the owners of capital who buy the sources of income streams in order to acquire the income from them; the suppliers are the enterprises or persons who produce the sources of permanent income streams with a view to selling them. A demand curve and a supply curve can be drawn along conventional lines and the intercept will be the price.

To begin with, assume a community in which there are no

3. Milton Friedman, *A Theory of the Consumption Function* (Princeton, Princeton University Press, 1957). See esp. Chs. II and III.

4. The approach presented here follows closely that of Milton Friedman in *Price Theory* (Chicago, Aldine, 1962), Ch. 13.

sources of permanent income streams capable of being reproduced. Let it also be assumed that this community is in a state of equilibrium "in the sense that productive services are being produced in the right proportions to produce the right amount of goods."[5] Under these assumptions, the supply of permanent income streams, i.e. the number of available dollars per year, is fixed. In this case, then, the supply curve is a vertical line when drawn on the conventional demand and supply diagram. Consider what would happen if the price of these permanent income streams were below the price that is consistent with the preferences and motives of the demanders for acquiring and holding sources of permanent income streams. Few or no persons would be willing to sell and conversely many persons would be willing to buy. This sequence implies that many persons would be willing to give up some current consumption in order to buy the source of a permanent income stream. But since the supply is fixed there would be no way for some persons to acquire more of them unless other persons were prepared to sell. Thus what would happen under these assumptions is that the price of permanent income streams would be bid up. As it rose, a price would be reached at which the market would be in equilibrium, in the sense that at this price no one in the community would be willing either to dispose of or to acquire additional sources of income. A sequence of adjustments of this type would bring the price up to its equilibrium level, but *it would not bring about any economic growth* because of the assumed vertical supply curve.

Assume now that the supply curve of permanent income streams were to slope positively and that it were not to shift over time. In this case, an adjustment on the part of the demanders who started from a price below the long-run

5. Ibid., p. 246.

equilibrium intercept would proceed over time, as before, toward the equilibrium price. When this was attained it would be the same (high) price already indicated for a vertical supply curve, provided the underlying preferences and motives of the demanders were the same. The only real difference between these two cases would be that some economic growth would occur as a consequence of the bidding up of the price of permanent income streams.

Assume now that the state of preferences and motives of the demanders for acquiring and holding the sources of permanent income streams remained constant over time. Under this assumption what would be the slope of the long-run demand curve for permanent income streams? Because the concept of capital on which this analysis is based is all-inclusive, including human as well as nonhuman capital, "there is no reason to expect the demand curve for permanent income streams to have a negative rather than a positive slope."[6] The most plausible presumption is that under this assumption there is a horizontal demand curve for permanent income streams.

Under the assumption that the long-run equilibrium de-

6. Friedman's reasoning is as follows: In a community of this type "income (Y) must be equal to rW, where r is the interest rate and W is wealth, since all wealth has been capitalized. $\frac{1}{r}$, the price of a source of a permanent income stream, is then the ratio of wealth to income. Now this ratio of wealth to income is a 'pure' number free from absolute units (except for a time dimension). Why should the desired value of this ratio depend on the absolute level of either the numerator or denominator? Indeed, what standard of comparison is there by which to regard one level of wealth as 'large' or 'small' except *relative* to another or *relative* to income; or one level of income as 'large' or 'small' except *relative* to another or *relative* to wealth? But if the community desires to maintain a fixed ratio of wealth to income regardless of the level of income, this implies a horizontal demand curve for permanent income streams." See *Price Theory*, pp. 247–48.

mand curve of permanent income streams is horizontal, what would happen to the price of the income streams in the event that the supply curve shifted downward as a consequence of the fact that the enterprisers who produced these sources of permanent income streams found ways of producing them more cheaply than formerly? One approach to the question of price determination is to assume that the shift of the supply curve is small and so gradual that demanders purchase enough additional income streams over time to maintain the price at its former level. This approach implies a small movement to the right along the horizontal demand curve as the adjustment is made to a small, gradual shift in the supply curve. An alternative approach is to assume that the downward shifts of the supply curve of permanent income streams are sufficiently large and rapid over time so that the price of these income streams falls and thus gives rise to a short-run disequilibrium. Under this assumption there would be a price effect upon the demand for these income streams, and in essence there would be a short-run demand curve that sloped negatively. A part of the demand analysis of an adjustment along these lines can then be treated in terms of its price elasticity.

How then will the demanders adjust? The second of these two approaches implies two types of adjustments on the part of the demanders of permanent income streams, one based on the price elasticity of the short-run demand curve and the other based on returning to the horizontal demand curve consistent with the long-run equilibrium preferences and motives of demanders. Assume the price elasticity of the short-run demand curve were unity (–1.0). In this case, if the downward shift of the supply were to reduce the price at the new intercept by 5 per cent, the demanders would proceed to increase their purchases by 5 per cent. In addition, the demanders would gradually bid up the price over time, compelled by their preferences and motives for acquiring and holding sources of permanent income streams, in returning to a long-run equilibrium.

This approach of determining the price of permanent income streams helps clarify a number of problems that arise in explaining the economic behavior of farmers who are bound by traditional agriculture. Whenever the price of income streams has become high, so high that the intercept of the supply and demand curves is along the long-run equilibrium horizontal demand curve, there will be zero (net) investment. Under these circumstances, the lack of any net savings and net investment is not to be attributed to a lack of thrift, or to a lack of entrepreneurial talent among farmers, or to imperfections in the capital market, but to the high price of the available sources of income streams. Clearly then the critical problem is to determine why the supply of permanent income streams in traditional agriculture is so costly.

The suppliers of the sources of permanent income streams hold the key to economic growth in the sense that when they are able to produce them cheaply the stage is set for the savings and investment necessary for growth. The study of growth, therefore, must concentrate on what is meant by, "they are able to produce them cheaply" and on what the circumstances are that make this possible. It means, in terms of the above analysis, that the price at which additional income streams are supplied is at or below the long-run equilibrium price. For the price to continue below this price over decades it would be necessary for the supply to continue to shift downward at a rate per decade that would be sufficient to offset the equilibrating force of the demander.

It may be helpful at this point to apply this approach briefly to two types of growth situations.

A NON-GROWTH TYPE

The essential characteristics of this type have already been indicated. To recapitulate, suppliers are unable to produce sources of income streams cheaply enough to induce the demanders to purchase any new (additional) sources. The price is high, and in conventional terms the rate of return to investment is accordingly low. The sources of some old income streams may be sold and purchased but the community acquires no new sources over time. The income of the community is the sum of the yield of all of the sources of income. To rephrase this in the usual language of economists, the income of the community is equal to rC, where r is the rate of return and C is an all-inclusive measure of the stock of capital (a formidable concept). The reciprocal of r, $\frac{1}{r}$, is then the price of the sources of the income streams, and it is also the ratio of capital to income. The ratio may be treated as a "pure" number free of absolute units except for a time dimension.

As a matter of convenience, let twenty-five dollars be the price of the source of a one-dollar permanent income stream in a non-growth type community. On this hypothesis, r would be .04 (a rate of four per cent) and the ratio of (all) capital to income would be twenty-five to one.

A GROWTH TYPE

Whereas all communities of a non-growth type are likely to have particular fundamental economic characteristics in common, this clearly is not true of all communities attaining economic growth. Some may be entering upon growth after a long period of stationary equilibrium. Some may be showing an unusually high rate of growth following a war seriously impairing one set of factors that can be replaced rapidly. Some may be coming to the end of a long period of substantial growth and may be approaching a long-run stationary equilibrium. All of these and still others will be put aside at this point in order to concentrate on a particular type of growth. There are some communities (countries) that have been attaining substantial growth per decade for many decades. Moreover, the annual rate of growth per decade has neither declined nor risen appreciably over time. This, then, is a type of growth in which the suppliers have continued to find ways of producing additional sources of income cheaply in terms of the preceding analysis. Consequently the supply curve has been shifting downward at such a rate that the price at the intercept of the supply and demand curves continues to stay relatively low. The suppliers by this test have been able to offset the equilibrating force of the demanders, which would have raised the price had the supply not shifted downward over time at the rate it did.

Here too it will be convenient to indicate some of the relevant numbers that may be associated with this type of growth. Let the price of a source be ten dollars for a one-dollar-per-year permanent income stream. Under these economic circumstances, let savings be ten per cent of permanent income. Implied in the relation of savings to income, capital to income, and more important, of the price to the amount of additional sources of income purchased is a moving growth "equilibrium," the key to which is the relatively low price at which suppliers are able to produce the additional sources of income.

6 PRICE OF INCOME STREAMS FROM TRADITIONAL AGRICULTURE

Farmers in *Penny Capitalism* are renowned for the low state of their reproducible capital. Once again the puzzle: why, in view of the meager stock of such capital and the implied scarcity of capital to increase agricultural production, is so little capital added over time to the existing stock? Why is the rate of net capital formation so low? If capital is really scarce, the inference would be that the rate of return is high and the inducement to save and invest is strong. But there is little evidence to support this inference. What evidence there is is quite to the contrary, which in turn would seem to imply that capital is not scarce in these communities. Is it possible for capital to be both scarce and abundant, both dear and cheap, at one and the same time? The implied behavior with respect to savings and investment is indeed a puzzle.

RELATIVELY HIGH PRICE OF INCOME STREAMS HYPOTHESIS

To explain the behavior that is under consideration the following hypothesis is proposed:

> *The price of the sources of income streams from agricultural production is relatively high in traditional agriculture.*

The theoretical basis of this hypothesis is presented in the preceding chapter. The purpose here is to examine a number of arguments against the hypothesis, to look at the data of two communities for clues bearing on the hypothesis, and to conclude with some major implications. Another aim is to show that this hypothesis provides a unifying explanation of a wide array of empirical behavior pertaining to savings and investment of poor communities, behavior that has baffled investigators.

An alternative formulation of this hypothesis would be that the rate of return to capital is low in traditional agriculture. Although it will be convenient occasionally in the exposition that follows to treat a low rate of return to investment as the equivalent of a high price of the source of an income stream per unit of time, the "price" hypothesis has not only marked analytical advantages but, as already noted, it also avoids some confusion and circularity. To recapitulate, it avoids the confusion that arises when an interest rate is treated as if it were the rate of return to investment, and it avoids the circularity that may arise when the stock of capital is determined by capitalizing the income stream of a source by an interest rate.

The traditional reproducible sources of income from agriculture in a poor community consist of irrigation wells and ditches, animals for draft and for food, simple equipment and hand tools, seeds, and structures in which to store crops. Acquired traditional skills are also a source of income although as a form of capital they are not bought and sold. Thus, in order to improve their skills, people invest in themselves. In accordance with the above hypothesis, when the demanders of additional sources of permanent income streams are restricted to these traditional agricultural factors of production, the prices of these factors will be high in relation to their marginal yields expressed in terms of real income.

What is at stake analytically in this hypothesis is anything but trivial. Suppose the hypothesis is consistent with relevant, observable behavior in these poor communities; it would mean that all of what has been written based on the belief that the rate of return to investment in traditional factors is high is not valid. A correct analysis would have to rest on a low rate of return. Thus, clearly, it really matters whether the hypothesis here proposed stands or falls when it is put to the test.

ARGUMENTS AGAINST THE HYPOTHESIS

Before turning to some empirical evidence, it may be helpful to clarify particular issues by commenting briefly on several quite obvious arguments that can be leveled against this hypothesis. Money lenders in poor agricultural communities often exact a high rate of interest, which may imply that by this market test the rate of return to investments in traditional factors of production is also high. There is the argument that it is self-evident that there is little reproducible capital in poor agricultural communities, and therefore such capital must be scarce and dear in terms of rate of return. Still another argument is based on the large historical movements of capital out of Western Europe into many poor communities such as those under consideration. These transfers of capital were generally in response to the differences in the rate of return to investment and therefore, so it is held, the rate of return in the poor communities must have been high relative to the then prevailing rate of return to investment within the European countries.

The factual question of the net rate of return that money lenders obtain will be held in abeyance, although what is charged and what is collected under these circumstances could make a large difference. Suppose, however, that the net rate were inordinately high by normal standards but that these loans were used predominantly to straighten out the consumption streams of particular families who were not demanders of reproducible material capital and of land as sources of permanent income streams. Suppose also that the loans were not used to invest in human capital. The market for consumption loans could be a different market from that for the permanent income streams under discussion. Furthermore, even when there are some loans strictly for agricultural production, some of these may entail high risk uses of funds, and for these it is to be expected that the charges of the money lender would be high.

The statement that communities are poor because they have so little capital, and therefore the rate of return to capital must be high, appeals strongly to common sense. It has also long been an accepted tenet of economic thought that the rate of return is in general high in poor communities because the supply of reproducible material capital is thought to be meager relative to labor and land. To say that this is not necessarily true may imply a paradox. If so, it can be resolved. As a matter of economic logic, if a community has had many decades to accumulate capital, and it did so for a time and then discontinued doing so, it would be logical to relate a low rate of return to the discontinuation even though only a small stock of reproducible capital had been amassed. But the stock of such capital is sometimes surprisingly large, as is evident from the data presented in the note following this chapter. The main burden of the hypothesis advanced here is that the observable rate of return to investment is low, and it is therefore very misleading to accept a common-sense notion that the opposite is true. The apparent paradox would then be resolved for reasons implied in the hypothesis.

The last of the opposing arguments mentioned above may appear to be the most compelling of the three. Why did Western Europeans, during the decades before World War I, make many investments in poor communities of the class under discussion if it were not to profit from a higher rate of return than could be realized at home? In answering, it will not do to catalogue the exceptional cases where capital moved in the other direction.

Economists who have accepted the tenet that the rate of return to reproducible material capital in poor agricultural communities is high have not been unaware of particular circumstances in which some capital has been transferred from poor to rich countries. Prosperous coffee growers in Guatemala not infrequently have invested their savings in the United States, and so have nationals of other poor countries. Some of them have invested their profits from crops, beef, wool, lumber, oil, and other minerals not at home but abroad in one of the rich countries. The explanation given for these apparent exceptions runs in terms of special circumstances related to risk and uncertainty and to a propensity to hoard wealth. It is of course true that nationals and others in some poor countries who make these transfers have been confronted by a large measure of political instability. The risk and uncertainty that political instability entails can be large enough to more than offset the otherwise apparent favorable rate of return to local investment. The explanation based on a preference to hoard wealth by accumulating and holding funds on deposit in a rich country has had little to recommend it, because such hoards would seem to be an integral part of the process of coping with uncertainty; it is not a separate or additional factor in these circumstances.

Exceptions aside, however, there are those who hold fast to the belief that the rate of return to investment in these poor countries is in general high because it is self-evident that reproducible capital is in short supply relative to the available labor and the endowment of natural resources, and because there must have been an incentive to have induced the earlier large capital movements into these areas. There are nevertheless strong reasons for not accepting this interpretation of the facts in testing the hypothesis advanced here. Consider, first, the matter of the relative amount of reproducible capital. In Senapur, India, which is based on irrigated agriculture, the stock of this capital is impressively large, e.g., there were 480 bullocks used as draft animals on a little over a thousand acres. In growing field crops, bullocks may be a more important factor than land, measured by value productivity. In the note that follows, in examining factor shares in poor agricultural communities it will be shown that such capital (service) is, as a matter of fact, a large production input where irrigation agriculture predominates.

The strongest reason for rejecting the above belief is that

the earlier capital exports from Western Europe to many poor communities were not used to increase the stock of the precise forms of the traditional factors of production already in existence. Capital from abroad was not employed to increase the number of bullocks, hand-dug irrigation wells, small surface ditches to carry the water to nearby fields, to make or purchase simple hand tools and equipment of the kind employed in Senapur. It was used instead for new forms of capital, i.e., for transport facilities, factories, some power installations, and means of communication. Some of it was used to establish plantations to grow special crops for export which were produced by means quite different from those that characterized traditional agriculture. Moreover, those who provided the capital from abroad did not turn the new structures, equipment, and varieties of export crops over to inexperienced people to manage, operate, and plant. The key personnel with the capabilities to perform these important tasks also came from abroad, along with the capital. In other words, both new forms of material capital and of human capital in terms of new skills were introduced. It was not a matter of merely multiplying the traditional forms of capital and old skills. *It is this distinction between the old and the new forms of capital that is basic to the analysis of investment opportunities in agriculture.*

It is hard to obtain precise, detailed data that can be treated rigorously in testing the hypothesis here proposed. The hand of poverty does not keep records of the kind required for this purpose. No doubt there are some bits and pieces among the many studies that have been made of the agricultural economy of poor communities. It is, however, beyond the scope of this study to examine all of these systematically in the hope that some usable data may thus be found. Two studies, however, have been examined for clues bearing on this hypothesis. They were drawn upon earlier in determining the allocative efficiency attained in agriculture in poor communities. It will be recalled that both of them were undertaken as anthropological investigations.

PANAJACHEL, GUATEMALA

Penny capitalism keeps no capital accounts. People can ill afford to record the niceties of depreciation and obsolescent rates, estimates showing net capital formation, and the return to capital. Hoes, axes, and machetes are used. But there are no specialized tools that go with carpentry and masonry. It is doubtful whether there is "a screw driver . . . in any Indian's tool chest. There are no smiths. Plows are not used; the wheel is not used (not one Indian family has a cart or wheelbarrow or anything of the sort—even a pulley)."[1] The crude network of hand-dug ditches to divert water from the river to the fields is simple and adequate.

How much would a dozen more hoes, a couple more ditches, a few more domestic fowl, several extra packages of seeds, or bags of crude fertilizer made from coffee leaves have added to production in 1936? If modern chemical fertilizer mixed to meet the soil requirements of the valley had been applied, the additional output would have been large. But given the technical properties of the coffee leaves and of the other inputs that were used, it is doubtful that the rate of return to expenditures in any of them could have been high.

1. Sol Tax, *Penny Capitalism,* Smithsonian Institution, Institute of Social Anthropology, Publication No. 16 (Washington, U.S. Government Printing Office, 1953), p. 27.

The stock of wealth belonging to the Indians, carefully catalogued by Tax, came out as follows:

Land, including coffee and fruit trees and irrigation ditches	$20,417	
Domestic animals	803	
Tools	680	
		$21,900
Houses (328)	3,870	
Household furnishings and supplies	2,335	
Value of clothing	3,500	
		9,705
Total		$31,605

Although the value of all domestic animals came to only $803, the income from this source was a meager $1,260—less than the cost of the feed, salt, and labor to care for the animals. If one subtracts "cats and dogs" (259 of them) from these accounts, a small profit remains for depreciation and return to the investment.[2] Tax observes, however, that to have invested more in domestic animals would not have been warranted; he singles out raising chickens and the fattening of a few hogs as poor business.[3] In growing crops (the main business) about $1,400 was spent for seed and fertilizer (coffee leaves), and $216 for tools. But there are no signs to suggest

2. Ibid., Table 40, p. 118.

3. In the total economic context so ably set forth by Tax, it is not plausible that chickens and hogs were less productive enterprises than the others. Had the price of fat hogs or of eggs and poultry been declining, a lag in adjusting to the lower product prices might have been reason enough for Tax's observation, but no such alteration in relative prices seems to have occurred.

that anything but a low rate of return could have been had by extending these forms of capital at their margins.

Although coffee land was not for rent, the data on costs and return to coffee production support a gross return to coffee land of about 8.8 per cent.[4] Since some land was had by renting, a clue to the rate of return is implicit in the relation between the value placed on the land and the gross rent. The Indians in this community rented from others 15 per cent of both the hill land and the delta land they cultivated in 1936. The hill land was selling for about $8 per acre, and a gross return of 9.8 per cent is indicated.[5] The rent and cropping data pertaining to delta land do not permit as firm an estimate of the gross return to the $150-per-acre land in this class.[6]

4. The relevant data Tax provides are: yield, 562 pounds selling at an average price of $4.50 per hundred wt. (p. 115) produced $25.29, minus labor and materials costs of $9.86, leaving $15.43 per acre on land valued at $175 per acre (p. 84), hence an 8.8 per cent gross return. There are 39.4 acres of coffee land, none rented. The total land area at the disposal of this community was about 255 acres.

5. There were 111.5 acres of hill land. Although Tax places the rent at $1.41 per acre, it is possible from the cash rent data in Table 14 of Tax's study to weight each subclass by size and cash rent payment. This procedure gives cash rent per acre of $1.26. Tax's estimate of the value of this land is $8 per acre and, since the rotation is 10 crops followed by 6 fallow years, the average rent is 79 cents per acre per year, or a gross rate of return of 9.8 per cent.

6. By weighting the parcels of delta truck land rented for cash reported by Tax in Table 14, the average gross rent comes to $27.90 per acre. The main difficulty here is to establish a basis to adjust for the substantial part of the delta land devoted to milpa (corn) for which the rent is much less. Unfortunately no delta milpa that rented for cash is shown in Table 14. Then, too, rotation patterns are exceedingly complex when it comes to allocating these rents over a whole rotation cycle.

Still another clue: a microcosm of the G.N.P. of this tiny sector sets forth the shares at factor costs.[7] The share available for management, profits, and gross rent from all land belonging to the Indians of this community is $1,770. Even if all of this were attributed to rent, the gross rate of return to land would have been only 8.7 per cent.[8]

What then is the net return to land? The gross return includes an array of costs that are difficult to identify and measure. Real estate taxes were small. However, the government required every adult to work on the highway one week every six months without pay. There were communal costs of cleaning the main irrigation ditches annually and repairing the damages after the river had been on a rampage. Still other extensive community services are listed, the costs of which may have settled against land.[9] More conventional than these is the depreciation of the private network of irrigation ditches and of the buildings used for production. There is the aging of the coffee trees (39 acres) after their prime and of the 2,690 fruit trees. The hill land is subject to some erosion, and the practice of fallowing and of leaving some land idle bears on the costs of maintaining the soil. Then, too, management must have some value in penny capitalism. Whereas the three estimates of the gross rates of return to land were between 8.7 and 9.9 per cent, it is likely that the net rate of return to land was 4 per cent or less.

7. Tax, Tables 37 and 38, p. 116.

8. Tax shows the 1936 value of agricultural products as $26,278 (Table 38). The costs shown in Table 38 are $24,131; adding to this $380 for rent paid in produce gives $24,511. The rest, $1,767, is profit earnings of management, and rent to land. The land had a value of $20,417 (p. 84).

9. Tax, Table 16, p. 86.

Even so, it was not free of risk and uncertainty. Land was accordingly capitalized at a high ratio to rent. Stated another way, a one-dollar income stream produced by land in Panajachel, subject no doubt to considerable risk and uncertainty and to this extent not a "permanent" income stream, was very dear, costing in the neighborhood of twenty-five dollars.

SENAPUR, INDIA

In Senapur there is a large stock of material capital; in this respect it differs greatly from Panajachel. The two communities, however, would appear to have one basic economic attribute in common, namely a low rate of return to investment in all forms of capital customarily used in agricultural production. In Senapur draft animals—bullocks—are a major factor of production. The stronger and larger animals are purchased from fairly distant communities that specialize in producing them. They are expensive production inputs in the sense that they have a relatively short life and the feed bill is large. Over the years much has been invested in the land for irrigation. The irrigation facilities, which include not only ditches but also surface reservoirs called "tanks" and expensive wells, depreciate and require much maintenance. In short, reproducible material capital is one of the major factors in agricultural production in Senapur.

Data presented by Hopper[10] and the account he gives of production activities are all consistent with the hypothesis that the rate of return to additional investment in any of the traditional factors of production is low. The return to the market value of land is in all probability about three per cent.

10. W. David Hopper, "The Economic Organization of a Village in North Central India" (unpublished Ph.D. dissertation, Cornell, 1957).

The stock of this capital in Senapur in 1954 was about as follows:

	Rupees (*in thousands*)
Land cultivated	2,323
Land not cultivated	274
Wells	266
Tanks	76
Bullocks	74
Implements	9
Total	3,022

Hopper classifies the land by types and estimates the value and the cash rent per acre of each class of land. The relation between the price of land and rent was complicated by the then pending or recently enacted land reform laws. To estimate the price of land, the sales prices on 19 land transfers were used. To determine the rental rates, the records of 51 parcels of land rented for cash, comprising 114 acres, were employed. The cash rents were exceedingly low relative to the price of land. The estimates shown below would represent a rate of return of less than one per cent.[11] But these

11. The table that follows gives the underlying estimates:

Land Class[a]	*Acreage*[a]	*Value per acre (rupees)*[a]	*Range in rents per acre (rupees)*[b]	*Average rent per acre (rupees)*[b]	*Per cent return to owner (of 1%)*
Kachiyana	1.4	3200			
Goir	75.1	3000	14–38	20	.67
Palo I	362.1	2750	12–31	16	.58
Palo II	279.7	2360	8–30	13	.55
Palo III	58.0	1710	6–24	9	.53
Kiyari I	32.9	2200			
Kiyari II	194.3	1830	6–28	9	.49
Kiyari III	166.9	1100	3–14	7	.63
Total	1170.4				

a. Hopper, p. 92, Table 7.

b. Ibid., p. 94, Table 8. In Table 40, p. 255, there are 114 acres of land rented for cash in 1954 and a total rent of 1,400 Rs., or 12.3 Rs. per acre rent.

cash rents are not the full rentals because there are some concealed payments, including understandings that when a "landlord needs labor services the renter stands ready to meet this need."[12] In a decisive test of the allocative efficiency of Senapur farmers, Hopper found that the marginal product of land was equal to about three per cent of the then prevailing price of land.[13]

CONCLUDING IMPLICATIONS

Consider, first, the investment of private capital for profit. The hypothesis here advanced would explain why so little foreign capital has been invested in traditional agricultural factors. Even under the protection of colonialism, foreign capital did not find such investments attractive. Nor were investments to develop plantations an exception because they introduced a substantial set of nontraditional factors of production. The hypothesis would also explain why so little domestic capital is invested per year, or per decade, to increase the existing stock of reproducible agricultural factors traditionally employed in these poor communities. The inducement to save for this purpose is exceedingly weak.

Consider, next, the results from public investments to increase agricultural production. Here, too, the hypothesis would explain the poor results from public investment restricted to traditional agricultural factors. On the other hand,

12. Hopper, p. 93.

13. W. David Hopper, "Allocation Efficiency in Traditional Indian Agriculture," *Journal of Farm Economics* (forthcoming). The pattern of double cropping, broken to leave the land idle one crop in six, gives five crops in three years. The estimated "implicit marginal product of land" averaged "Rs. 72.62 per year over the three years, or about three per cent on the Rs. 2,360 price of a 'standard' acre."

the excellent results achieved by many countries from public investments in nontraditional factors, e.g. in a scientific agricultural research establishment and an agricultural extension service, are also thus explainable.

The most important implication of this hypothesis relates to economic growth: in traditional agriculture the factors of production on which a community depends are expensive sources of economic growth.

A Note on Factor Shares

There are two erroneous views about factor shares in low income agricultural communities. One is that the stock of reproducible material capital is always relatively small and, therefore, even if the rate of return were high the share of total income produced by such capital would be small; the other erroneous view is that rent from land is always one of the larger shares. Baffling as it may seem, the stock of reproducible capital is often large in traditional agriculture. But that rent from land should be small or even zero in some cases should not be surprising. The purpose of this note is to show that the amount of material capital represented by structures, draft animals, and the like is frequently underrated and that land as a natural endowment is sometimes overrated in evaluating the factors of production in traditional agriculture.

Turning first to rent, it is as a rule a larger share of the income in poor than in rich countries. There are two useful empirical propositions about rent in this connection: (1) the way agricultural land is commonly measured, the rent it produces may account for as much as 25 per cent of the income of some low income countries and for less than one per cent in a high income country;[14] (2) as per capita income rises

14. Phyllis Deane, "The Implications of Early National Income Estimates for the Measurement of Long-Term Economic Growth in the United Kingdom," *Economic Development and Cultural Change, 4*

with economic growth, rent from agricultural land as a rule declines relative to other sources of income.[15]

But there are two reasons why these empirical rules are not inconsistent with the fact that in some low income agricultural communities rent from land as a natural endowment is a small share of total factor income. The first of these is based on situations in which the land used for farming is of very low productivity. It can be land that produces no rent whatsoever. Under these circumstances, neither the logic on which Ricardian rent is based nor the observed rent from such land supports the view that rent is always large relative to total factor income.

For a tribe of nomads grazing animals on no-rent land, the income share of land is of course zero. For such nomads, one would find the following factor shares.

	Per cent
Land	0
Livestock and labor	100
Total	100

The other reason why land is often overrated arises from the fact that in many communities rent is in large part a return to capital that has been embedded in such land. It is important to distinguish between the original natural en-

(November 1955), in examining the social accounts of England and Wales in 1688, in Table 1, places the (national) personal income at £48.6 million, rents at £13 million, and rent on houses and homesteads at £2.5 million, thus leaving the £11.5 million for other rents, which is 23.7 per cent of all income payments. In the United States the income attributed to farm land in 1955–57 was .6 of one per cent of net national product. See the author's essay, "Land and Economic Growth," in *Modern Land Policy* (Urbana, University of Illinois Press for the Land Economics Institute, University of Illinois, 1960), p. 27.

15. In recent decades this proportion has been declining rapidly in the United States and presumably in other high income countries.

dowment and the capital embedded in it. In many long-settled communities much has been invested over generations in leveling the land so that water can be applied, in sinking wells to provide water, in making ditches to distribute the water, and in drainage to check soil salinity. These facilities depreciate and require maintenance. Thus, in a densely settled agricultural community on a highly fertile delta that is irrigated, rent from land can be a relatively large part of all factor income because the rent includes a return to highly productive land and, in addition, a return to a large quantity of capital that has become an integral part of such land.

Turning next to the share of factor income attributed to reproducible material capital, as already implied it can be a substantial share in some low income agricultural communities. Yet in Panajachel, Guatemala, despite a good deal of irrigation, a very large share of the income went to labor. In Tax's *Penny Capitalism,* the Guatemalan Indians had an economy in which the factor shares in 1936 were about as follows:

	Per cent
Labor	84
Land	10
Seed, tools, etc.	6
Total	100

But the widely held view that all poor agricultural communities, e.g. all of those in India, employ relatively little reproducible capital is quite contrary to fact. It may come as a surprise to find that such capital, even without counting what is embedded in land, is in some cases larger as a factor of production than either land or labor. Estimates of production inputs for irrigated agriculture of Punjab attribute 41 per cent of all inputs to reproducible capital (see Table 3). If half of the productive value of land were reproducible capital, it would be about 53 per cent. Bullock power and implements in such cases are a large factor.

TABLE 3

Production Inputs of Agriculture of the United States and of Irrigated Agriculture of Punjab, India

Inputs	*Weights in per cent*	
	United States (*1949*)	*Punjab* (*1947–48*)
Labor	33	34
Land (unadjusted for structures)	19	25
Power and machinery	26	30 (bullock power and implements)
Seed, feed, and livestock	13	5 (only seed)
Fertilizer	2	4 (manure)
Other	7	2 (water charges)
	100	100

Sources: The estimates for the United States are based on the study by Zvi Griliches, "The Sources of Measured Productivity Growth: U.S. Agriculture, 1940–1960," *Journal of Political Economy, 71* (August 1963), Table 2, p. 336. The Punjab, India, estimates are from Farm Accounts in East Punjab, 1945–46 to 1947–48, cited by Nasir Ahmad Khan, *Problems of Growth of an Underdeveloped Economy* (Bombay, Asia Publishing House, 1961). Professor Griliches derived the weights for U.S. agriculture for 1949 by means of a cross-sectional aggregate production function. The Punjab weights are based on "expenditures." Rent comprises both rent paid and imputed rent on the land owned by the cultivators and the land tax.

A comparison of agricultural production inputs of the United States and of Punjab, given in Table 3, shows labor to be 33 and 34 per cent respectively, and power from bullocks and implements in Punjab larger than power and machinery in the United States. After adjusting agricultural land, by allocating 36 per cent of the land to farm buildings in the United States and 50 per cent to irrigation structures in Punjab,[16] each of the three conventional factors holds

16. The adjustment for farm buildings is from Zvi Griliches's study referred to in Table 3; the adjustment for Punjab is strictly a judgment.

virtually the same relative position in the two countries, as the following estimates indicate:

	United States agriculture (per cent)	*Punjab irrigated agriculture (per cent)*
Labor	33	34
Land (adjusted)	12	13
Reproducible non-human capital	55	53
Total	100	100

The first conclusion of this section is that rent from land is a small part of total factor costs in some poor agricultural communities. This conclusion is quite compatible with economic theory, although the possibility that rent can be small or even zero is sometimes overlooked in considering the contribution of the several factors to agricultural production. The second conclusion is that reproducible material capital is relatively large as a factor of production in many poor agricultural communities. It will not be easy to make this conclusion feel at home in the house that economists have built. To make it even more of a stranger is the fact that the factor share of reproducible capital is large in some of these communities even though the rate of return on such capital is low. If the rate of return were always high, the stock could be small and the share relatively large; but if the rate of return is low, as it is in many of these poor agricultural communities, the matter would indeed be baffling given the conventional economic conception that the stock of reproducible capital in poor agricultural communities is small.

7 PREFACE TO INVESTMENT PROFITABILITY

Traditional agriculture can be transformed into a relatively cheap source of economic growth. The purpose of the following chapters is to clarify what such a transformation entails and what means are required to accomplish it efficiently. There is a *command* approach based on the use of political power not only to reorganize agricultural production but to administer farming activities. Alternatively, there is a *market* approach based predominantly upon economic incentives to guide farmers in making production decisions and to reward them in accordance with their allocative efficiency, although this entails particular public investments and state activities. The command approach has led to the establishment of large collective and state farms and to the development of a state authority charged with the responsibility of making the basic production decisions. Such a state authority decides what is to be produced, specifying both the class of farm products and the amounts to be produced. The strategic inputs to be used are rationed, and the output is subject to compulsory deliveries to the state.

The market approach does not simply mean leaving all investment to the market. Nor would it succeed if it were restricted to ways and means of reducing the imperfections of the capital market with a view to increasing the amount of capital made available to farmers. While there is room for improving the terms at which such capital is made available to farmers, these improvements will not bring about the desired transformation. The additional amounts required by farmers for this purpose per year are as a rule not large and for the most part they will be forthcoming from internal savings once profitable new agricultural factors are supplied. But of primary importance is the investment to produce a supply of new agricultural factors that will be profitable for farmers to adopt. Investment also is required to improve the capabilities of the demanders for such factors. These two classes of investment, however, require considerable public expenditures and the organization of particular public activities to serve the agricultural sector.

The essential difference between these two approaches is not that a command system in which the key decisions are centralized excludes additional investment in agriculture or that a market approach in which relative prices integrate consumption, investment, and production decisions excludes any and all state intervention in matters pertaining to agricultural production. That the increases in the number of tractors, combines, and threshers and in the tonnage of fertilizer can be large under a command approach is clearly demonstrated in the case of Czechoslovakia.[1] On the other

1. Alexander Bernitz, *A Survey of Czechoslovak Agriculture,* U.S. Department of Agriculture, ERS—Foreign—35 (September 1962), Tables 14 and 15. Also Gregor Lazarcik, "Factors Affecting Production and Productivity in Czechoslovak Agriculture, 1934–38 and 1946–60," *Journal of Farm Economics, 45* (February 1963), 205–18.

hand, for example in the case of Mexico, a market approach entails government experiment stations for agricultural research and public activities to improve the capabilities of farm people in addition to the more conventional public expenditures for roads, transport, and irrigation facilities. But the difference in the efficiency between these two approaches is large, and the reasons why this is the case will be examined later in some detail. When the market approach is adopted, the difference in the efficiency of *absentee* and *resident* production decisions in farming becomes relevant, and it will therefore be necessary to consider the economic basis for the inference that private resident decision-making is the more efficient of the two in farming.

The particular new factors of production that are required in making this transformation are presently in a large box labeled "technological change." It will be necessary to remove them from this box, sort them, and find ways of making them available and acceptable to farmers who are bound by traditional agriculture. Once this has been done, it will be clear that the suppliers of these particular factors of production, and farmers in their role as demanders of them, hold the center of the stage. This chapter is addressed to the modest task of arranging the stage.

The arrangement is based on differences in economic opportunities. It is the age-old difference between an established way of acquiring farm products (food, fiber, skins) and a new way which wins out because it is cheaper. Over uncounted centuries there has been an advance in knowledge that has been useful to people in farming, and, as a consequence, there have been many agricultural transformations. Cultivated cereals, roots, and nuts replaced wild species. Many times over a cultivated plant that had long been the best was replaced by a more productive variety. In growing cotton, and notably in the case of corn, large improvements were realized ages ago from hybridization. Domesticated animals replaced wild animals as a source of meat and skins, and some were selected and trained for draft work. Irrigation replaced dry land farming in some areas, and crop rotations and the use of manures proved profitable. Thus again and again people transformed a particular traditional agriculture by adopting and learning how to use a new factor of production.

Clearly, in a number of countries, the increases in agricultural production over the last several decades have been large. These increases represent responses on the part of farmers to new economic opportunities. The opportunities in general have not come from the opening up of new farm land for settlement nor have they originated primarily from a rise in the relative price of farm products. They have come predominantly from more productive agricultural factors.

At the outset of this study the recent rates of increase in agricultural production of a number of countries were presented. Viewed *ex post,* these countries presumably had been experiencing favorable opportunities. The increases in production, for example, in Denmark starting about 1870 bespeak a favorable turn in opportunity for growth, particularly so on the part of the agricultural sector. The record of agriculture in Japan since about 1900, and especially since World War II, implies that the opportunity for this growth has been favorable. Mexico also, during recent decades, has achieved not only a high rate of growth generally but the rate of increase in agricultural production appears to have exceeded that of the economy as a whole. Agricultural production in the Soviet Union has increased substantially. Still another case is that of the agricultural sector in Israel in the 1950s. Except for the Soviet Union these countries have continued the forward momentum. The inference may well be that except for the Soviet Union these countries have maintained favorable opportunities for agriculture.

Still on an *ex post* basis, the opportunity for growth must have taken an unfavorable turn in the Argentine, Chile, and Uruguay following the 1930s. The apparent recent events in China can be interpreted as a most unfavorable turn, so much so that agricultural production has declined. Meanwhile, the two classic poor agricultural communities—Panajachel, Guatemala, and Senapur, India—have had little or no opportunity for growth. Panajachel has continued as of old, for nothing really has happened to break the virtual non-growth circumstances. Senapur, meanwhile, is beginning to feel some impulses which represent new, small opportunities for growth.

Like a trading floor on which commodity futures are bought and sold, one observes throughout the world different groups of suppliers and demanders of agricultural factors of production haggling over the price. Toward the rear of the stage, close to the entrance, there is a stand marked "traditional agriculture." The group at this stand is the quietest of the lot; there are few transactions, and the price of the factors is very high relative to what they contribute to income. At the center and in front is the group representing modern agriculture; here there is much activity, but the going price is low, especially so compared to the price prevailing at the stand of traditional agriculture. There also are a number of other more or less active groups of suppliers and demanders and the range in price among the different groups is wide, but none is as high as in traditional agriculture.

Although the suppliers and demanders attached to each group are in equilibrium in relation to the going price at their respective stands, there is a massive disequilibrium among the stands. The opportunity for economic growth from agriculture in most poor countries in which farming has as yet not been modernized is a function of this massive disequilibrium. A complete transformation would imply an approximation to a worldwide equilibrium in the return to the relevant agricultural factors of production. The attainment of this transformation also implies a revolution in the productivity of agriculture because most of agriculture is as yet far from modern.

A classification of the agricultural opportunities for growth is implied in the attributes of the economic disequilibrium under consideration. The aim here is to classify the agricultural sector of countries or communities to show where agriculture stands. The earlier, much simplified dichotomy consisting of a growth and a non-growth type, while useful at that stage in the analysis, is much too restrictive to cope with the wide range of empirical situations that can be observed. It would, of course, please one's taste for economy and elegance to discover a fundamental attribute that would reduce these classes to a simple dichotomy. But this is a pleasure that cannot as yet be realized.

As has already been suggested, a threefold classification is here proposed of which the first two are fairly homogeneous. But the third class is composed of many subclasses.

1. *Traditional.* All agricultural sectors in which the state of the arts and the state of preferences and motives for holding and acquiring agricultural factors as sources of income streams have remained approximately constant for a long period—long enough for suppliers and demanders of agricultural factors to have arrived years ago at a particular long-run equilibrium—belong in this class. Its critical economic characteristic is the high price of the sources of permanent income streams from agricultural production. Panajachel is the prototype of this class.

2. *Modern.* The essential attributes of agriculture belonging to this class are as follows: Farmers employ modern agricultural factors of production and there is only a small lag between the development of any new factor of production and its adoption, provided it is profitable. For farmers in agriculture of this class to be supplied with additional new, profitable factors of production, it is up to the research establishment of the country to discover and develop them. To do this, it is necessary for such a country to invest in activities that contribute to an advance in knowledge and its application to agricultural production. Furthermore, in general, in a country of this type the preferences and motives for holding and acquiring sources of permanent income streams have not arrived at a long-run equilibrium with respect to the supply price of such sources. The price of the sources is therefore in general low, although the rate of increase of agricultural production is as a rule not as high as in many countries of the transitional class, the third in this classification, because of the relatively slow growth of the demand for farm products.

3. *Transitional.* Between the first two classes already identified, there exists a vast economic disequilibrium. The fundamental source of this disequilibrium is the large inequalities in the price of agricultural factors relative to their value productivity in agriculture. This means that the disequilibrium under consideration does not in general originate in inequalities in farm product prices between the two classes. Nor does it originate primarily in differences in the way farms are organized in traditional and modern agriculture, provided they are not under a command system. Any country or community in which agriculture acquires a supply of one or more profitable, nontraditional factors of production enters this transitional class. It is a large class consisting

of a wide array of agricultural sectors in terms of the stage at which agriculture has arrived and in terms of the number of new profitable agricultural factors that are ready and available for adoption.

Thus one sees three stands at which the suppliers and demanders of agricultural factors of production are selling and buying. One also sees that the manner of trading that characterizes each of them is of minor importance. What matters are the economic forces that sooner or later will bring all three together into a single well-integrated market, i.e. the market of the relevant reproducible agricultural factors. These forces can be harnessed efficiently only by means of investment.

Before turning to the analytical core of this discussion, it will be helpful to consider several unsettled issues bearing on the economic organization of agriculture. These issues relate to the size of farms, to the control of economic decisions by the state, and to the incentives that guide and reward farmers for efficient farming. Are there large gains to be had from increasing the size of farms? What are the economic functions of the state in developing a modern agricultural sector that is efficient in the allocation of resources? Do farmers in traditional agriculture show little or no response, or even perverse responses, to normal economic incentives? These are exceedingly troublesome issues when it comes to the economic organization of agriculture. Not only are the relevant facts hard to come by, but there is also a vast amount of confusion rooted in political dogma. It is to these issues that the next chapter is devoted.

8 FARM SIZE, CONTROL, AND INCENTIVES

The question of farm size looms large in the ideological controversy over how agriculture should be organized. There are as a rule hidden political objectives that thwart economic discussion. Once these are made explicit and separated from the economics of producing agricultural products, it turns out that the underlying economic issues are predominantly empirical questions.

The findings of this study give a new perspective to the role that farm size plays in modernizing agriculture. Consider, first, the finding that traditional agriculture is niggardly in the meaningful sense that it is an expensive source of economic growth. In searching for the economic attributes of traditional agriculture, it became clear that small farms, or for that matter large farms, are not essential attributes. Take next the finding that traditional agriculture can be transformed into a highly productive sector and thus into an inexpensive source of economic growth by means of investment. Here, too, it became evident that the types of investment that are essential in transforming traditional agriculture are not dependent, for example, upon the establishment of large farms. The size of farms may change as a consequence of the transformation—they may become either larger or smaller—but changes in size are not the source of the economic growth to be had from this modernization process.

Strongly held beliefs about the "proper" farm size make it difficult to examine this question without incurring the risk of being misunderstood. An appeal to the concept of "returns to scale" is as a rule barren because the transformation of traditional agriculture always entails the introduction of one or more new agricultural factors, and therefore it gives rise to a process in which the critical question is not one of scale but of factor proportionality.

The real world reveals a welter of differences in farm size. Small farms and fragmentation of fields often go hand in hand. Large farms and unskilled farm people are frequently joined. Thus land reform tilts in one case with fragmentation and in the other with depressed, illiterate farm people who are trapped on large land holdings. But by what test are such farms inefficient because of size?

In many countries there are part-time farms in and about industrial centers. In the Soviet Union there are millions of tiny plot farms within the confines of large state and collective farms. There are farms employing a fleet of large tractors and many more farms on which a small tractor is used. The question of farm size is not restricted to field crops and grazing land in which the land area is important. It arises also in the production of poultry and dairy products. Are very large farms ultimately the efficient way to produce farm products?

The locus of the person or agency making the production decisions in farming is an important factor determining the efficiency of agricultural production. The locus under consideration depends upon farm size and whether the decisions are under absentee or resident control. One approach is to relate the control of production decisions to the ownership of agricultural factors, which may be private or public. Private control obviously can be vested either in absentee or resident ownership. But whether the control over production decisions is vested in persons who reside on farms or in persons who are far removed from farm operations, and whether the farm is large or small, what matters is the relationship of each of these components to the state of economic information on which production decisions are based and the state of economic incentives and rewards for making efficient decisions.

These then are the principal issues to be examined here. But it would be a gross understatement to say that there is only a lack of clarity about these issues. There are some real puzzles, there is obviously much confusion, and there is a large realm of dogma. Economic theory and empirical studies can do much to resolve the puzzles and to reduce the confusion that arises from them. Hopefully they may also dislodge politically entrenched dogmas.

It may be useful to identify some of the more important dogmas and doctrines bearing on these issues. Although the transformation of agriculture in the United States has gone ahead at a rapid pace, there is nevertheless a strong doctrinal view. A comment on it may provide some perspective on other doctrines. There is still a long-cherished belief in the United States that agriculture is *the* basic sector of the economy, that farm people possess social values superior to those of the rank and file of urban people, and that the family farm is the "natural" economic unit in farming.[1] These are particular manifestations of *agricultural fundamentalism.* In contrast, in recent decades a wholly different doctrine has been espoused in some poor countries. It holds that industry is always *the* basic sector in achieving economic growth, that farm people are not only bound by tradition but are innately more backward than nonfarm people, and that a substantial part of the farm labor force has a marginal productivity of zero value. The appropriate label for this doctrine is *industrial fundamentalism.*

The failures of public programs to transform traditional agriculture into a highly productive sector in a substantial number of countries are a consequence of policy decisions to establish very large operating units in agriculture. Back of these decisions are political goals, which are then supported by particular beliefs about "returns to scale" that have long been an integral part of Marxian thought. The conception of agricultural production advanced by Marx is strongly biased in favor of large farms. This conception rests on the elemental belief of the superiority and necessity of large producing units.[2] Formally it is a proposition to the effect that large farms can produce farm products at less real cost than either small or medium-sized farms. Practically it has meant the larger the producing unit in agriculture the more efficient it will be. This then is the doctrine of *gigantic farms.*

Policy and programs related to agricultural production

1. Lauren Soth, *Farm Trouble* (Princeton, Princeton University Press, 1957), Ch. 2, "The Shibboleths"; Joseph Ackerman and Marshall Harris, eds., *Family Farm Policy* (Chicago, University of Chicago Press, 1947). The old southern agrarianism is of a different vintage; see William H. Nicholls, *Southern Tradition and Regional Progress* (Chapel Hill, University of North Carolina Press, 1960).

2. David Mitrany, *Marx Against the Peasant* (Durham, University of North Carolina Press, 1951), Ch. 2.

are seriously burdened by still another doctrine. In its crudest form it presumes that farmers do not respond, or if they do they respond perversely, to normal economic incentives. All manner of price and income policies can be and are promulgated under this doctrine. If it is true that farmers do not respond to prices, why not keep farm product prices low and thus reduce the costs of food while a country develops its industry? Compulsory deliveries of farm products of course follow, and by then the economic incentives required for efficient agricultural production have been greatly impaired. But the doctrine can be given a different twist. When the agricultural production of a country continues to exceed the demand for farm products at some fixed support price that is high, the doctrine declares that any reduction in the support price would not help correct matters; it would only make them worse because, so it is held, farmers would respond by producing even more. From the point of view of political expediency, it is a convenient doctrine. In some high income countries, it is effectively used to keep some farm product prices too high; in some low income countries, it is badly used to do exactly the opposite, i.e. to keep some farm product prices too low. There are even more extreme effects upon resource allocation when one or more factor prices are deemed to be socially undesirable and are thought to serve no economic purpose in managing an economy. Thus, for example, rent on agricultural land may be suppressed where all property rights in land are vested in the state. In such cases, this rent doctrine has seriously impaired the capacity of the planning and control apparatus to allocate agricultural land efficiently (including buildings, irrigation facilities, and other structures attached to the land).

Even when an investigator is not carried away by doctrinal drifts, he will find it hard to navigate his inquiry through the tangled empirical float. An important part of the task is to recognize the essential components and to search for the connections among them. Farm size is related to the specialization of functions, the locus of control over production decisions, the state of information on which these decisions are based, the rate at which traditional agriculture is being transformed, and the risk and uncertainty inherent in the incentives that guide and reward those who produce farm products.

SPECIALIZATION OF FUNCTIONS

Organized research. It would be absurd to make the size of the farm depend upon its capacity to undertake modern agricultural research. It would be better for each farm to produce the tractors, combines, and other machinery it needs than to undertake research. Even if all of the farms in any one state in the corn belt were combined into a single farm it is doubtful whether a first-rate research center would be profitable on even so large a farm. Clearly this is one of the specialized functions that is beyond the capacity of farms regardless of how large they are. Some plantations undertake some research and some large landowners also have such pretensions, but they are not capable of approaching even remotely an optimum in the research activities they can support and organize. But is it not premature to preclude the possibility that very large farms could have their research laboratories? No doubt there are classes of applied research where this is a possibility, but even the largest corporations make relatively few basic research contributions.[3]

3. D. Hamberg, "Invention in the Industrial Research Laboratory," *Journal of Political Economy, 71* (April 1963).

The reasons why agricultural research is necessary and why it is beyond the capacity of farms can be readily summarized. Most modern agricultural factors of production are specific to the biological and other circumstances of the country in which they have been developed. When a country dependent upon traditional agricultural factors decides to acquire and adopt modern factors, it will not suffice merely to import and use the existing forms. Instead it will be necessary to develop new forms appropriate to the particular circumstances of the country. To do this it is necessary to start with the scientific theories and principles that have been established and, on the basis of this knowledge, develop the appropriate factors, which entails a considerable research effort. There is still another critical fact, i.e., the enterprise undertaking such research cannot capture all of the benefits from its activities; then, too, the enterprise is subject to important indivisibilities because it requires a staff of scientists and costly specialized facilities. It is wholly impractical for farms, no matter what their size, to be efficient in undertaking all of the necessary agricultural research. If that is the way it is approached, there will be too little research, and even that which is undertaken will as a rule be exceedingly costly.

But large landowners and farmers who operate large farms in poor countries are often victims of the belief that if there is any agricultural research worth doing they can best do it on their own farms. They do not understand the economics underlying the activities of agricultural experiment stations. Consequently one observes in some of these countries that a division in interest arises, with large farmers opposing public expenditures for agricultural research and small farmers favoring such expenditures. In Uruguay, for example, because of this apparent division of interest the small farmers in the southern part have an agricultural experiment station serving them while the very large farms in the rest of the country are on their own.[4]

One of the anomalies where agricultural production is administered by the state is the inefficiency of a major part of the scientific and technological research pertaining to agriculture. One might have expected the performance in agricultural research to have been outstanding under this type of organization, especially so in the Soviet Union with its scientific tradition and research achievements in other areas. But the record is quite otherwise. The basic research lacuna has been in bringing the biological sciences to bear on agricultural production. A deep-seated doctrinal bias has seriously impaired this important branch of agricultural research, despite the fact that the agricultural research function has not been made an integral part of either state farms or of collective farms and has not been starved by a lack of funds.

Producing modern inputs. As a rule, new varieties of plants and better breeds of animals, once they are known and available, can be multiplied on farms without developing stresses on the size of farms. But there are some important exceptions. For example, firms that specialize in producing hybrid seed corn are more efficient in producing it than most farms. So it is with some animals and with eggs to introduce superior types of poultry. At some stage hatcheries become efficient as specialized firms. While it is obvious that farms

4. In the early 1940s the writer had an opportunity to examine the agricultural research then under way in Uruguay. The contrast between the relevance and competence of the research of the small experiment station and that of a lonely, poorly trained college graduate employed by a large farmer as a "geneticist" was as great as one would expect.

often produce the draft animals they need, they cannot produce farm tractors. Nor can they produce chemical fertilizers and insecticides.

"Producing" information. As in the case of agricultural research, it is hard to imagine farms so large that they would be efficient in establishing their own agricultural extension service. Where there are published materials—pamphlets, newspapers, farm journals—and radio and television programs disseminating some of this information, this part can be had by farmers whether they operate large or small farms, provided they are literate and in other ways capable of understanding what the information means.

There is no substitute for a system of product and factor prices as a means of providing farmers, regardless of the size of farms, with essential economic information. Those who operate large farms can in some cases afford to acquire some expert economic advice that small operators cannot afford. A strong argument for a system of forward prices for agriculture is that such a system would augment the efficiency of small farmers by reducing somewhat the price risks and uncertainty they otherwise must face without information from experts.

ABSENTEE OR RESIDENT CONTROL AND FARM SIZE

Absentee ownership in agriculture is commonly associated with land and the structures that go with land although other agricultural factors also may be the property of persons not living on farms. There are many and sundry tenancy arrangements. There are also corporations, partnerships, and managers through which absentee owners administer agricultural factors they own. Absentee arrangements are in general inefficient.

The economic basis for this inefficiency rests on the proposition that in approaching modern agricultural conditions the current operating decisions and the investment decisions in farming are not only subject to many small changes which entail spatial, seasonal, mechanical, and biological subtleties that cannot be routinized, but also constantly require the adoption of new, superior, agricultural factors that are developed as a consequence of the advance in useful knowledge. The decisions to deal with these subtleties, and especially to take advantage of the advance in useful knowledge, cannot as a rule be made efficiently under absentee arrangements for the simple reason that it is not possible for the absentee parties to become sufficiently informed. Nor have absentee owners been successful generally in developing the necessary incentives and in delegating responsibility for decisions. Nor have the many farm tenancy reforms been wholly successful in this respect. The proposition formulated above implies the following hypothesis: under competitive conditions, as farmers adopt and learn how to use modern agricultural factors an increasingly larger part of all farming is taken over by owner-operators. This means, to state it another way: where there is competition, that part of farming under absentee arrangements decreases relatively because of inherent inefficiencies.

This hypothesis is consistent with an array of data for the United States. There is no doubt that farmers have been successful in applying many new superior agricultural factors. Nor is there any doubt that owner-operators have been gaining ground competitively. It will be convenient to use "farm output per man-hour" devoted to farming as a proxy for the modernization process. This proxy rose only a little between 1910 and 1930, from an index of 45 to 53 with

1947–49 equal to 100. But since 1930 there have been the following developments:

	Farm output[5] per man-hour (1947–49 = 100)	Percentage of all farm operators[6]		
		Owner-operators	Tenants	Managers
1930	53	56.7	42.4	.9
1940	67	60.7	38.7	.6
1950	112	72.7	26.8	.4
1960	208	(1959) 79.0	20.5	.5

Also relevant is the fact that between 1929 and 1960 the net farm rent to persons not living on farms declined from 8 to 6 per cent, and payments in the form of farm mortgage interest from about 7 to 4 per cent of the total net income from farming.[7] In Western Europe and in the United Kingdom, although there have been reforms in farm tenancy laws the trend also has been in favor of owner-operator farming units.[8]

5. Based on Table 19, *Changes in Farm Production and Efficiency,* U.S. Department of Agriculture Statistical Bulletin 233 (July 1961).

6. From Table 633 of *Agricultural Statistics 1961* (U.S. Department of Agriculture). Owner-operators include both full and part owners. The percentage of all land in farms owned by full and part owners rose less sharply; it accounted for 49.8 per cent of all land in farms in 1930 and rose to 55.4 per cent in 1959. There is a strong presumption that the percentage of all productive assets owned by farm operators has risen substantially more than that shown for land in farms.

7. Based on estimates for 1929 in Table 686 of *Agricultural Statistics 1950* (U.S. Department of Agriculture), and for 1960 in Table 692 of *Agricultural Statistics 1961.*

8. A. K. Cairncross, "The Contribution of Foreign and Indigenous Capital to Economic Development," *International Journal of Agrarian Affairs, 3* (2), (April 1961), 101. See also William H. Nicholls, *Industrial-Urban Development and Agriculture in São Paulo, Brazil, 1940–50* (Nashville, Tenn., Dec. 20, 1962, mimeo.) p. 225. "In the Tennessee Valley, as in São Paulo in 1940, the more industrial zones showed a moderate tendency to have relatively more owner-operators and few renter-operators."

It is true of course that where the absentee owner is a recently retired farmer who knows from long experience the particular farm he owns and who resides in the community in which the farm is located, or where father-son leases and arrangements to transfer the property gradually are adopted, "absentee" private ownership is not necessarily subject to all of the inefficiencies that characterize this form of ownership generally. But these exceptions aside, absentee private ownership of farms is an inefficient arrangement.

What are the absentee implications of state ownership of agricultural factors of production? There are marked similarities between absentee state and private ownership. Nor should the correspondence come as a surprise because it is of the essence of state ownership that some of the basic decisions in farming are made under *absentee* conditions. The economic basis for inefficiencies from this source is the same as it is in the case of absentee private ownership, and the empirical evidence on what happens in practice strongly supports the same inference.[9] Yet despite the correspondence it would be a serious error in examining the effects of state ownership upon agricultural production not to distinguish between the different power structures of states. Obviously, in a Soviet-type state, state ownership of farm land is only a detail in the totality of the controls the state has of agricultural production. The state bureaucracy also has ownership of all of the other material means of production and in addition it has a monopoly of power, including control of the

9. An exception to this conclusion arises when there are areas of land that entail multiple uses, such as grazing, forestry, water control, and park services. Although the limitations inherent in absentee public ownership and administration are none the less real than in the case of pure agricultural production, there is no experience to support the view that private ownership can cope successfully with large indivisible, multiple uses of land.

ideological apparatus. Although the adverse effects of the absentee component inherent in state ownership of agricultural factors is real and significant in a Soviet-type state, it is compounded by other and much stronger instruments of control.

PSEUDO-INDIVISIBILITIES AND FARM SIZE

The doctrine that farms must be very large to be efficient has made the tractor into a symbol of the indivisibility of modern agricultural factors. It holds that the tractor that matters in this connection is not only a big tractor but a fleet of big tractors. The rest of agriculture must then be tailored to fit fleets of big tractors. But tractors so conceived are a pseudo-indivisibility for it is no secret that tractors can be made to order from a wide array of sizes and types and can also be combined in farming in all manner of ways. A tractor can of course be so big that it draws not only a dozen plows but a grain seeder and a harrow and other attachments all in one operation, for example in growing wheat under particular conditions. At the other end of the array, a tractor can be so small that for draft work it is equivalent to a water buffalo in growing rice. Then too, there are tractors that crawl on their own steel aprons and others that roll on wheels and are especially suited for row crops. There are also those that move and drive the machine they draw, ranging from large self-propelled grain combines to tiny self-propelled lawnmowers. Where human effort (labor) is cheap relative to the price of other agricultural factors, a one-man (or family) farm may be efficient with a small garden-type tractor; on the other hand, where human effort is relatively dear, a one-man farm may be efficient with a combination of two or even three tractors that differ in size and type. It requires very special conditions for a fleet of big tractors to be efficient, conditions which in fact rarely exist.

Big tractors and many hoes. But when a pseudo-indivisibility becomes the basis of organizing the production of agriculture it leads to an inefficient allocation of resources. Clearly this is what has happened in the Soviet Union where large power-driven machinery has been forced to the extreme. By tailoring agriculture to big tractors, it has forced agriculture into an absurd, bimodal structure of farm sizes, i.e. exceedingly large state and collective farms and tiny plot farms, a bimodal structure based on big tractors and many hoes.[10] Both types are highly inefficient. Suppose that on the large state and collective farms only the costs of tractors and the machinery to match them mattered; even then it would be more economical to have a complementary assortment of tractors consisting of large, intermediate, and small types instead of only very large tractors. But labor, management, land, and other forms of material capital are exceedingly important. Meanwhile, the millions of plot farms are restricted to many hoes and to an extremely intensive use of labor. Nowhere in Western Europe is peasant farming so inefficient in the employment of labor as it is on the plot farms in the Soviet Union. Suppose these plot farms were increased to no more than 10 acres and suppose small hand (garden-type) tractors and complementary machines and equipment were made available; total agricultural production in the Soviet Union would rise sharply and chiefly of those farm products that are presently in short supply. Even

10. Theodore W. Schultz, "Big Tractors and Many Hoes: A Comment on Soviet Agriculture," University of Chicago, Office of Agricultural Economic Research, Paper 6006 (August 1960, mimeo.). This paper is based on observations of the author while in the Soviet Union during the summer of 1960 as a guest of the Soviet Academy of Science.

so, given the resources of the Soviet Union millions of 10-acre farms, along with large state and collective farms, would be far from optimum sizes. Thus, although agricultural production would be much more efficient than it is now, it would still be an inefficient bimodal set of farm sizes. Clearly the tractor is a pseudo-indivisibility.

Real indivisibilities. What then are the indivisible factors of production in modern farming? Consider only the inputs employed in farming. Superior varieties of seeds, better breeds of livestock, chemical fertilizer, insecticides, tools, implements drawn by animals, tractors, and related machinery and electric motors where electricity is available are rarely of this class. But the typical farmer, or the typical farm administrator where farms are under absentee control, is as a rule indivisible. This particular indivisibility does not require a large farm, however; on the contrary, given the kind of operating and investment decisions that characterize most of modern agricultural production, one man viewed as indivisible does not necessitate a large farm. Herein is the key to the proven efficiency of family-sized farms, for example in Japan, Denmark, and the United States. But even here a qualification enters, because in communities where nearby off-farm jobs are readily available on both a part-time basis and a full-time basis the contributions of a human agent become divisible and part-time farming becomes possible; and it can be efficient.[11]

SUPPRESSION OF RENT

Misconceptions about the economic function of rent are abundant, and where they have been applied they

11. James F. Thompson, "Part-time Farming and Resource Productivity in Western Kentucky" (unpublished Ph.D. dissertation, University of Chicago, 1962).

have impaired the efficiency of farming. Whether rent from land is deemed to be unearned in the sense that it is a consequence of increases in the demand for farm products over time, or whether it is earned as a return to investment in structures that become an integral part of the land or simply as the value productivity of a particular material factor of production, rent performs a necessary economic function in the allocation of resources in farming. Thus any suppression of rent impairs the signals and incentives that are necessary to guide and induce farmers to use farm land efficiently.

Both classical and Marxian doctrines have fostered misconceptions about rent. The Ricardian conception made landowners the recipients of increases in income over time that was deemed to be unearned, and the allocative function of rent was lost sight of. The Marxian conception, which is based on Ricardo, has been dogmatized into complete state ownership of all land and into a complete suppression of rent in the allocation of land in production. In a Soviet-type economy, farm land and the productive services of irrigation facilities and other farm structures are rationed by those who administer agricultural production. Once rent has been suppressed, sundry ad hoc measures are used to capture the value productivity of land and of its appurtenances. These measures are now well known: compulsory deliveries of farm products at some nominal price, the sale of farm products to the state at a low fixed price, and assessments against collective farms for various welfare purposes. And earlier, the imposition of a high monopoly price for the services of the machinery and tractor stations may also be viewed, among other things, as such a measure. Yet, with the possible exception of assessments for welfare purposes, one of the effects of all of these measures has been to reduce the value productivity of farm land. They have neither captured the many subtle differentials in value productivity that characterize farm land nor have they performed the economic function of rent in allocating land in agricultural production. Thus the suppression of rent has been the cause of many inefficiencies in the utilization of land in farming.

Another misconception pertaining to rent is associated with the widely held belief in poor countries that agriculture must provide a substantial part of the capital required for industrialization. Since rents are often high in agriculture and landlords are deemed to be unproductive, the natural source of this capital is the rent from farm land. It is then presumed that an efficient way to acquire this rent is for the government either to purchase the main farm products from farmers at some low price and then sell them at a substantial profit, or simply to maintain low farm prices and thereby keep food prices and wages below what they would otherwise have been, thus reducing the costs of industrialization. This approach to acquiring capital from agriculture does not capture the true rent, i.e., the value productivity of farm land. It always impairs the allocation of resources between agriculture and the rest of the economy. A classic demonstration of the adverse effects of this approach occurred in Argentina under the Peron regime: the agricultural production of Argentina was seriously reduced by this approach, although it produced a large amount of public revenue for a few years.

There is an alternative approach that does not suppress the allocative function of rent. A government can of course acquire revenue for industrialization or for other purposes by taxing farm land, by assessing a capital levy against such land, or by outright expropriation. But to acquire this revenue and at the same time to maintain the allocative function of rent it is necessary to distinguish between that part of rent which is a return to the site value embedded in land and that part of rent which is a return to the reproducible capital structures of land and to the entrepreneurial function of the landowner. Capital structures that are an integral part of land entail maintenance and depreciation. All told in the United States presently, the net rent to landowners not living on farms is only about half of their gross rent.[12] Even so, in this estimate of net rent no allowance has been made for the value of the entrepreneurial contribution of landowners.

The key to the approach under consideration is for the government to make sure that enough of the value productivity of the land continues to be vested in farmers (or landowners) to provide an incentive to allocate the land efficiently. One way to attain this aim would be by means of a capital levy on each parcel of land equal to a large part of the capitalized value of the permanent income from this source, thus leaving a small part of this value with the landowner—enough to provide an incentive to allocate it efficiently in farming. Another way would entail an annual tax equal to a large part of the permanent income stream contributed by the site value of the farm land, which also would leave a small part of this income stream with the landowner, presumably sufficient to maintain the necessary incentive to induce the owner to allocate it efficiently. By these means, some public revenue can be had from rent without suppressing the allocative function of rent.

FARM PRODUCT AND FACTOR PRICES MATTER

The allocative function of product and factor prices cannot be dispensed with in transforming traditional

12. See Table 693, *Agricultural Statistics 1961,* U.S. Department of Agriculture.

agriculture. There is no efficient alternative. A command system, whether it operates through large or small farms, is inherently inefficient.

Whatever the motives for suppressing product and factor prices in agriculture, there is no end to the many ways in which this is done. The suppression of rent, already considered, should be viewed as a special case of a large set of such suppressions. It will not be necessary to elaborate on the others, because in principle the same reasoning set forth in the discussion of rent is applicable.

The root of the belief that some suppression of farm product and factor prices is feasible and desirable is of two parts. There is the view that farmers either do not respond to changes in these prices or respond perversely. This view has been examined in several different connections in this study and it has always proven to be false. The other view is that income can be transferred either out of or into agriculture, by either lowering or raising farm prices somewhat, without impairing the allocative function of such prices. In some low income countries, in which economic growth has become a major goal, one of the aims is to transfer some income out of agriculture to provide, as noted earlier, a part of the capital required for industrialization. In high income countries, especially those in which the agricultural sector has become highly productive, the government seeks to transfer some income into agriculture to improve the economic lot of farm people. But, regardless of the purpose of such income transfers, whenever they are made by means that either lower or raise farm product or factor prices, the allocative efficiency of such prices is impaired. In the case of the net rent from the site value of land, as set forth above, there is an approach for transferring much of this rent component to the government without suppressing the allocative function of rent.

But it is an exception in the sense that there is no comparable approach that is applicable to other agricultural factors or to any farm products which makes it possible to transfer income by means of prices either into or out of agriculture without reducing the allocative efficiency of factor and product prices.

There is always the choice of improving the allocative function of farm product and factor prices, or of supplanting them with other controls which always turn out to be inefficient. The improvements that matter are of several sorts: e.g., integrating local markets into larger markets, disseminating economic information about products and factors, reducing imperfections in the capital market as one way of lessening capital rationing in agriculture, pricing at marginal costs the services of irrigation and other facilities subject to indivisibilities and to scale requirements that preclude a competitive price, and investing in health, schooling, and other forms of human capital. Reducing the fluctuations of farm prices also belongs here.

The only reason for calling attention to the last on this list of improvements arises out of the fact that the particular inefficiencies inherent in widely fluctuating farm prices have been examined with care. Also, the proposal of forward prices for agriculture to cope with the adverse allocative effects of such price fluctuations is a logical and feasible improvement.[13]

13. See esp. D. Gale Johnson, *Forward Prices for Agriculture* (Chicago, University of Chicago Press, 1947).

9 FACTORS OF PRODUCTION CONCEALED UNDER "TECHNOLOGICAL CHANGE"

The approach of this study to economic growth is to apply the concepts of demand and supply to determine the price of permanent income streams. One of the important and necessary steps in using this approach is to find income streams that can be acquired at a price low enough to induce savings that will be invested in the sources of income streams. The question then is: *Where are these low-priced sources of permanent income streams?* Although there are many studies of economic growth, both theoretical and applied, they have contributed very little in providing an answer to this question. The main reason why they have not clarified the economic basis of the low-priced sources of income is a consequence of the fact that these particular sources are concealed under "technological change."

Zvi Griliches's and Dale W. Jorgenson's comments on an early draft of this chapter were very valuable.

Factors of Production Concealed

The main inferences of this study up to this point will serve as a preface to the aims of this chapter. There is at best little opportunity for growth from traditional agriculture because farmers have exhausted the profitable production possibilities of the state of the arts at their disposal. Better resource allocation and more savings and investment restricted to the factors of production they are employing will not do much for growth. Despite all that has been written on how to improve the mix of factors in poor communities, the increases in real income to be had from a better allocation of the existing factors are small. Even if such a penny economy were a *perfect* mixing machine in allocating each and every one of the factors at its disposal, the community would remain poor. A similar conclusion follows with respect to the growth to be had from increases in the stock of such factors. They are high-priced sources of additional income, and for this reason they provide little opportunity for growth. What this means is that agriculture will remain niggardly under such circumstances. Assume that the natural endowment is given. Assume also that there is no improvement in the level of skills although the labor force increases with the growth in population, and that there are no changes in the technical attributes of the reproducible forms of material capital although the stock of existing forms of structures, equipment, and inventories increases somewhat. Under these assumptions, economic growth from agriculture will be very costly. Because it is so costly, the many proposals to increase savings and to bring in outside capital in order to augment the rate of investment in existing factors—proposals that clutter the literature on economic development—are simply too expensive to be worthwhile. The relation between costs and return to investment in the factors of production is the basic reason why there is not sufficient inducement for people in these communities to save a larger proportion of their income to invest in such factors. The rate of return simply does not warrant the additional investment.

If it were true that all agricultural production were dependent wholly upon the factors of production employed in traditional agriculture, the growth prospects from this sector would be bleak everywhere. Or, if they were to differ only moderately, as they do between Senapur and Panajachel, the gains in production to be had from such differences would still be very small. But, as a matter of fact, the difference in agricultural factors between communities that depend upon traditional and modern agricultural factors is large indeed.

THE GAME OF CONCEALING FACTORS

The neglect already referred to stems largely from the manner in which the factors of production are treated in studying growth. Economists have fallen into the practice of dividing the productive agents into two parts, one of which consists of "land, labor, and capital (goods)" and the other of "technological change." But what is all too seldom recognized in making this division is that the term "technological change" is merely a bit of shorthand for an array of (new) factors of production that have been omitted in the specification of the factors. It is of course permissible to abstract from any and all new factors, but there is no logical basis for the belief that techniques are not factors of production. A technology is always embodied in particular factors and, therefore, in order to introduce a new technology it is necessary to employ a set of factors of production that differs from the set formerly employed.

There is much at stake in this issue analytically because of the apparent mistaken belief that a "technological change" can be treated as if it were logically possible to separate a technique of production from the factors of which it is a part. A technique of production is an integral part of one or more factors. When an all-inclusive concept of the factors of production is used, including not only all material forms of capital (which contains whatever useful knowledge is part of such capital) but also all human agents (which in turn contain the know-how that man acquires, i.e., skills and useful knowledge that are a part of the capabilities of labor), all techniques of production are completely accounted for. Thus, to repeat, the notion of a "technological change" is in essence a consequence of either adding, or dropping, or changing at least one factor of production.[1] Moreover, in many circumstances it may be no more difficult to specify, identify, and measure a new factor, the effects of which generate what is concealed under "technological change," than it is to do this for a traditional factor.

The analytical device of placing some things into a compound to be set aside, or to be held constant, is, as already noted, both permissible and necessary. Theoretical analysis proceeds in this way. So do empirical investigations, and properly so, when the factors in such a compound either remain constant in their effects on production or play only a minor role in altering production to the extent that they change over time. The concept of "technology," or "state of the arts," is such a compound. But when this compound becomes an important variable over time, as is the case in modern economic growth, the particular factors that are in it

1. The writer discussed some of these issues in "Reflections on Agricultural Production, Output and Supply," *Journal of Farm Economics, 38* (August 1956), 748–62.

must be examined and their economic behavior analyzed if growth is to be satisfactorily explained.

What matters then conceptually is that the technology used for production is an integral part of the productive agents employed. Since the productive agents include the human agent, the knowledge (or know-how, or "instruction") of how to employ each of the productive agents including himself is also an integral part of the factors of production. Accordingly, when all of the factors of production are completely specified, the technology is also specified. While the economic logic on which this conception of the factors of production is based is clear, its practical implications in studying growth can be clarified further by some examples.

Examples of the attributes of some agricultural factors. Dairy cows capable of producing 10,000 pounds of milk annually are far superior to those that can produce only 4,000 pounds. The process of replacing inferior by superior cows is a form of factor substitution, based on costs and return considerations that are concealed when all dairy cows are lumped together and the production effects of this factor substitution are treated as a residual and labeled "technological change." The same logic applies when hens that produce 100 eggs or less a year are replaced by hens that will produce 200 eggs. The nutritive value of feed stuff can be altered appreciably by mixing into it a (new) "feed additive," a distinct ingredient, which is produced for this purpose and for which there is a well-defined market. For some expository purposes, it may be convenient to refer to the adoption of such a feed additive as a technological change, but to explain changes in agricultural production it is necessary to treat the feed additive as a productive agent and to determine its costs and return. Moreover, as already implied, it is as identifiable and measurable as any of the traditional factors. Changes over time in the plant nutritive properties of fertilizer and in the relative supply price of fertilizer are another important example affecting agricultural production in recent decades. Improvements in skills and in knowledge that are useful in farming become integral parts of the human agent. To call such an improvement a change in "know-how," useful as it may be in exposition, conceals the fact that a new and better human agent has been developed at some "price" which is associated with a "return." Lastly, there is the classic example of hybrid corn analyzed by Griliches.[2] A bushel of open-pollinated and a bushel of hybrid seed corn are, for many purposes, identical. The ground on which each is planted is prepared in the same way. The same machinery is used to plant, cultivate, and harvest the corn. Yet in analyzing the production of corn, the open-pollinated and the hybrid seed are markedly different factors of production. Nor is hybrid corn some vague, unidentifiable source of "technological change"; on the contrary, it is a precise, identifiable, and measurable factor of production.

Changes in the supply of particular factors of production over time. Another approach to show the limitations of the notion of technological change is to examine changes in the supply of factors. The supply of some factors is quite properly treated as fixed. There are other factors that are correctly treated as produced means of production, and obviously the supply of these can be augmented. Still other factors are incorrectly treated as if they simply happened to come along. Land is presumably fixed in supply, but it is not given nearly as much weight now as was attributed to it by the older economists. Nevertheless, there are particular qual-

2. Zvi Griliches, "Research Costs and Social Returns: Hybrid Corn and Related Innovations," *Journal of Political Economy, 66* (October 1958).

ities in the natural environment and in human beings which are not augmentable; they are therefore qualities that represent factors, the supply of which is essentially fixed.[3] Capital goods are always treated as produced means of production. But in general the concept of capital goods is restricted to material factors, thus excluding the skills and other capabilities of man that are augmented by investment in human capital. The acquired abilities of a people that are useful in their economic endeavor are obviously produced means of production and in this respect forms of capital, the supply of which can be augmented. Studies of economic growth based on increases in man-hours worked and on increases in capital restricted to structures, equipment, and inventories, presumably with quality held constant, do not take account of the important changes that occur over time in the quality of labor and of material capital goods. The advance in knowledge and useful new factors based on such knowledge are all too frequently put aside as if they were not produced means of production but instead simply happened to occur over time. This view is as a rule implicit in the notion of technological change.

The history of economic thought related to this treatment of the factors of production is clear enough. Classical theory began by imposing a tripartite classification on factors and by holding the state of technology constant. But as economic growth occurred in reality, the state of technology not only changed but became one of the important variables increasing real income over time. Meanwhile, a good deal of apparatus for analyzing production had been developed, based on the assumption that the state of technology remains con-

3. In the case of man, the qualities that are not acquired but are inherited biologically are for all practical purposes "fixed" per man in any large population over any time span that matters in economic analysis.

stant. Thus, to reckon with obvious changes in the quality and forms of the factors of production and not forgo using this long-established intellectual equipment in which so much has been invested, as every graduate student knows, the notion of technological change has become fashionable to cover what are in fact ever-larger increases in income that are not explained by conventional concepts and measures of land, labor, and capital.

This is not to say that the term "technological change" may not be a useful device for some expository purposes. But it is not an analytical concept for explaining economic growth. To use it for this purpose is a confession of ignorance, because it is only a name for a set of unexplained residuals.[4] The usual errors of measurement aside, if the residual values attributed to it were small it would be tolerable, but when these residual values are large, as they are in fact in the kind of growth that has characterized modern countries, it leaves much of the real growth unexplained. A few economists are now addressing themselves to this matter. A comment on their efforts follows later in this chapter.

The original concept of the "state of the arts" is based on the assumption that there exists in man and in material things a pervasive set of qualities that are essentially fixed in supply, akin in this respect to the original properties of land. It was not deemed necessary to consider what the many components that made up the state of arts were like. But, when these components are altered, what is implied? It might

4. Moses Abramovitz, in his *Resources and Output Trends in the United States since 1870,* Occasional Paper 52 (National Bureau of Economic Research, 1956), saw this clearly when he pointed out (p. 11) that the fact that little is known about the causes of "productivity increase" is a "measure of our ignorance about the causes of economic growth." See also E. D. Domar, "On the Measurement of Technological Change," *Economic Journal, 71* (December 1961).

mean simply that the quality of at least one of the existing factors of production has been improved. Or it might mean that a wholly different factor of production has been introduced. The first of these, i.e. an improvement in quality, can also be treated as equivalent to a new factor of production. At this point it will be convenient to look upon both of these as new factors of production. Though the essential attribute of any technological change is no more or no less than the introduction of a new factor of production the use of which has become economic, in rigorous analysis there is no way of achieving a technological change in production except by introducing a new factor of production that differs technically in some respect from the old. An appeal to the concept of a production function will make this relation between new and old factors of production clear. A so-called "upward shift" of a production function requires the production effects of at least one new factor. Thus, if the specification of factors is incomplete in the sense that the new factor is not included, an observed production function based on such an underspecification may appear to shift upward as a consequence of the production effects of the new factor of production.[5]

Thus there are compelling reasons for rejecting the concept of technological change as an explanatory variable of economic growth. Analytically it conceals most of the essence of economic growth. To look upon technological change as "labor saving," or as "capital saving," or as neutral in this respect is meaningless unless the capital and labor components of the unspecified (new) factors of production are identified and made an integral part of the analysis. Once

5. The problem of specification in estimating production functions is pervasive in character. See Zvi Griliches, "Specification Bias in Estimates of Production Functions," *Journal of Farm Economics, 39* (February 1957), 8–20.

the new factors of production have been identified, one may of course find that they are substitutes for, or complements of, particular old factors of production. The notion of "technical horizons" is also meaningless in this connection and for the same reasons. The principal issue is that technological change is an unexplained residual which conceals most of the important sources of the relatively low-priced permanent income streams that induce the savings and investment related to growth. What is concealed under technological change then are particular (new) factors of production that are adopted and employed because it is profitable for firms to do so. In addition, since these new factors are produced means of production, the activities of discovering, developing, and producing them are essential parts of an all-inclusive concept of production. It is important therefore to examine the costs and return to investment of discovering, developing, and producing these new factors of production.

EXAMINING WHAT IS CONCEALED

The view of the sources of economic growth on which this study is based is not altogether new. There has long been an awareness of the importance of the advance in knowledge in increasing production. Suffice it to mention only a few of these. Alfred Marshall rated knowledge very high and considered it the most powerful engine of production.[6] Joseph Schumpeter attributed modern growth mainly

6. Alfred Marshall, *Principles of Economics* (8th ed. London, Macmillan, 1930), Bk. IV, Ch. I, p. 138. Ch. VI of Bk. IV treats schooling and compares Western Europe and the United Kingdom, and also the United States and the United Kingdom, in this respect. Marshall's *Industry and Trade* (London, Macmillan, 1919), is a much-neglected study of economic growth. See esp. his use of the "increasing returns" attributed to advance in science and technology in examining the economic history of Germany.

to sources other than increases in the labor force and increases in the stock of traditional forms of capital.[7] The treatment by Frank Knight of "all increase in 'useful' knowledge, regardless of what it is 'about,' "[8] as a produced means of production does not differ in principle from the approach of this study. E. F. Denison's[9] approach has the merit of introducing a number of important sources of economic growth that have been generally neglected. His concept of labor as an input comes close to representing the flow of the services contributed by labor because it is largely based on the earnings of the labor force. To the extent that it is, the increases in total earnings of the labor force are then distributed among a number of sources that alter the quantity and quality of the labor force. But his concept of capital as an input does not represent the flow of services contributed by capital. Increases in material capital are substantially underestimated

7. Joseph A. Schumpeter, *The Theory of Economic Development,* trans. R. Opie (Cambridge, Harvard University Press, 1951), p. 68.

8. Frank H. Knight, "Diminishing Returns from Investment," *Journal of Political Economy,* 52 (March 1944), 26–47. Knight at one time felt that the whole conception of "factors of production" should be discarded outright. In this paper he refers to the extreme position he took in 1928 (p. 33, n. 7) with respect to this issue, but he goes on to express doubts whether this should be done, although he continues to stress that the "problem of the classification of productive agents presents a serious dilemma for economic analysis."

9. Edward F. Denison, *The Sources of Economic Growth in the United States and the Alternatives Before Us,* Supplementary Paper No. 13 (New York, Committee for Economic Development, 1962). Denison allocated 27 per cent of the growth rate between 1929 and 1957 to increases in employment and hours and 15 per cent to addition to the stock of capital. Compared to these conventional sources, he allocates 23 per cent of the growth rate to increases in education of the labor force and 20 per cent of it to advancement in knowledge. (Since his estimates include some sources that had small negative signs, the above four estimates need to be adjusted downward slightly when related to the net growth rate. See Table 32, p. 266.)

because his concept of "advance in knowledge," which is essentially a residual, conceals a large flow of productive services that are an integral part of the contributions of material capital.

R. M. Solow[10] first entered upon this problem empirically by making estimates of an "aggregate production function" of the United States for the period between 1909 and 1949, based on capital and labor measured in such a way that neither was even remotely related to the flow of services produced by real capital and real labor. In view of the capital and labor components omitted, it is not surprising that his "function" shifted upward "at a rate of about one per cent per year for the first half of the period and 2 per cent per year for the last half." Although this study has won wide acclaim, it did not come to grips with the new factors of production underlying so-called technological change; it merely transformed the unexplained residuals into a sequence of upward shifts of a partial (not an all-inclusive) production function. In a recent paper, Solow[11] treats the formation of new capital goods as a "carrier" of new technical knowledge and in this way seeks to cope with the production effects of some of these new factors of production. Another treatment is that of W.E.G. Salter[12] relating technical

10. Robert M. Solow, "Technical Change and the Aggregate Production Function," *Review of Economics and Statistics, 39* (August 1957), 312–19.

11. Robert M. Solow, "Technical Progress, Capital Formation, and Economic Growth," *American Economic Review, 52* (May 1962), 76–86.

12. W.E.G. Salter, *Productivity and Technical Change,* Monograph 6 of the Department of Applied Economics, University of Cambridge (Cambridge, Cambridge University Press, 1960). See also L. Johansen, "A Method for Separating the Effects of Capital Accumulation and Shifts in the Production Functions upon Growth and Labor Productivity," *Economic Journal, 71* (December 1961), 775–82.

knowledge to techniques of production and introducing these techniques into the production function presumably as integral parts of the observable factors of production.

The criticism directed in this chapter at what is concealed in technological change is not intended to imply that the production function is a useless analytical tool. It is indeed a necessary tool. What needs to be done is to include not only the traditional factors but also the new factors that embody the new techniques of production. This is the approach that Griliches is pursuing with promising results. It entails taking account of improvements in the quality of both human and material inputs. The essence of this approach was clearly foreshadowed by Griliches in "Measuring Inputs in Agriculture: A Critical Survey."[13] The changes in the quality of capital loom large in this approach.[14] Improvements in human capital (education) also enter. Thus Griliches, in a progress report on his studies of agricultural productivity, observes that "Since any productivity measurement formula either implicitly or explicitly assumes something about the form of the aggregate production function for the industry and about the numerical values of its coefficients, many of the questions raised about the correctness of such measurement procedures can be investigated more easily by asking these questions directly about the production function."[15]

13. See *Journal of Farm Economics, 42* (December 1960), 1411–33.

14. Zvi Griliches, "Notes on the Measurement of Price and Quality Changes," in paper read at the Conference on Research in Income and Wealth, University of North Carolina, Chapel Hill, N.C., Feb. 3, 1962.

15. Zvi Griliches, "Agricultural Productivity: A Progress Report," University of Chicago, Office of Agricultural Economic Research, Paper No. 6205 (May 29, 1962, mimeo.), read at a meeting of the Econometric Society, Dublin, Ireland, September 1962.

IMPLICATIONS OF AN ALL-INCLUSIVE CONCEPT OF FACTORS

This approach to the sources of economic growth implies a theory of capital that includes all factors of production, i.e. land, all reproducible material means of production, and human agents. It implies also that by means of investment the stock of both human and material capital can be augmented. An optimum allocation of savings to investment requires equality in the rates of return between reproducible material and human capital forms, as well as within each of these two sets. Thus there is in principle a test for determining whether there is an underinvestment or overinvestment in either human or material capital.

Factors of production then are the sources of permanent income streams. The income streams are the flows of the (productive) services of these sources. To determine the weight to be given to a source (an input), it is not correct to measure labor in terms of man-hours, or a stock of material capital minus improvements.

A DEMAND AND SUPPLY APPROACH

Once the particular factors of production concealed under technological change have been identified, the problem of analyzing the sources of economic growth is substantially clarified. Two propositions have been presented. The first makes it clear that the economic basis of the slow growth associated with traditional agriculture is explained by the dependency upon a particular set of factors of production the profitability of which has been exhausted. The second proposition indicates that in order to break this dependency farmers situated in traditional agriculture must somehow acquire, adopt, and learn how to use effectively a profitable new set of factors.

The concepts of demand and supply are useful in analyzing the process of attaining the objective implied in the second proposition. This approach leads one to examine the roles that the demanders and the suppliers of the new profitable set of factors play and the economic basis for their behavior. The demanders in this case are the farmers in traditional agriculture. The suppliers are those persons (firms for profit and also nonprofit agencies) who discover, develop, produce, distribute, and thus make available to the demanders the new set of factors of production. What these suppliers do is obviously a production activity whether it entails discovering, developing, or producing factors that have been developed, or distributing such factors. But it is not so obvious that what the demanders do can also be treated as a production activity based on inputs that entail costs and render returns. The demanders may search for information about these new factors, and the process of searching can straightway be treated in a costs and returns frame of reference. The demanders also learn how best to use such factors which is, however, as a rule less direct than that which is implied by a "search for information." More important is the investment in human beings, through schooling and instruction. The next two chapters are devoted to these suppliers and demanders.

10 SUPPLIERS OF NEW, PROFITABLE FACTORS

Economic growth from the agricultural sector of a poor country depends predominantly upon the availability and price of modern (nontraditional) agricultural factors. The suppliers of these factors in a very real sense hold the key to such growth. When they succeed in producing and distributing these factors cheaply, investment in agriculture becomes profitable, and this then sets the stage for farmers to accept modern factors and learn how best to use them. It is also an inducement to increase savings and to develop institutions to provide credit for financing investment in such factors. These suppliers are indeed important.

But the suppliers have received little attention. Many of them have been treated as if they were wholly outside the pale of economics. They are the producers of the factors of production concealed under "technological change." Some of them engage in research and some in developmental activities. Some produce only information. They are not homogeneous either in what they produce or in the way they are organized.

This chapter considers mainly the cost of the productive services that the suppliers of modern agricultural factors provide in making such factors available and acceptable to farmers in poor communities. The cost of producing these services is of critical importance. It will be convenient to leave conventional production activities aside and to concentrate first on research and development that is required to adapt known modern agricultural factors to the particular conditions of the poor community and second on the economic basis of distributing these factors by firms for profit and by nonprofit agencies.

RESEARCH AND DEVELOPMENT BY SUPPLIERS

The principal sources of the high productivity of modern agriculture are reproducible sources. They consist of particular material inputs and of skills and other capabilities required to use such inputs successfully. The components in land and in man that are fixed by nature are generally of secondary importance. The reproducible sources are clearly of two parts, namely modern material inputs and farm people with modern skills. Although there are some examples of people with a high level of farming skills migrating to a poor community, this is nevertheless an exceptional way of acquiring such skills. In general, poor agricultural communities can acquire the necessary skills only by investing in their own people. There is, however, in modern material inputs much that can be imported.

But these modern material inputs are seldom ready-made. They can rarely be taken over and introduced into farming in a typically poor community in their present form. They must be fitted to the particular conditions of agriculture in the poor community. Differences in biological requirements are especially important. Many of them are associated with differences in latitude. For example, a variety of hybrid corn suited to Iowa will do better in Indiana than it will in Alabama. Breeds of dairy cows that are highly productive in the temperate zones are not up to tropical conditions. Soils, too, differ greatly from zone to zone, and these differences affect significantly plant, fertilizer, water, and cultivation requirements. There are very few reproducible agricultural factors in technically advanced countries that are ready-made for most poor communities.

In general, what is available is a body of useful knowledge which has made it possible for the advanced countries to produce for their own use factors that are technically superior to those employed elsewhere. This body of knowledge can be used to develop similar, and as a rule superior, new factors appropriate to the biological and other conditions that are specific to the agriculture of poor communities. This knowledge consists of established scientific theories and principles pertaining to plants, animals, soils, mechanics, and so on. The genetic principles underlying hybridization which have made it possible to produce some plants and animals having specific "hybrid capacities" are the foundation of all hybrid corn. It is however no simple matter to apply this knowledge about hybridization in developing a superior variety of corn for a particular corn-producing area. There are still some areas in the United States in which farmers continue to plant open-pollinated varieties for the simple reason that no hybrid variety has as yet been developed that is sufficiently productive and profitable in that area to warrant replacing the open-pollinated variety.

For a country to profit from the established genetic knowledge about hybridization or from other relevant knowledge, it is necessary to do what has been done during the last two decades and is being done by the government of Mexico and the Rockefeller Foundation to develop modern agricultural factors suited to the conditions of Mexico. The annual reports on the progress made in Mexico[1] are studded with statements like the following:

1. "In releasing a new white dent corn, hybrid H–507, 750 samples of about 2 lbs. each were distributed to farmers. . . . H–507 has shown a yield advantage of about 20% over the previously recommended hybrid (H–503) and about 35% over the best open-pollinated native varieties in the area."

2. "Repeated trials of introduced corns, such as U.S. hybrids, have verified the earlier observations that locally developed varieties from native materials are essential if serious difficulties arising from the use of non-adapted germ plasm are to be avoided."

3. In sorghum also United States varieties were found wanting. "Specifically, earlier varieties are needed in many areas, and varieties better able to set seed dependably at elevations above 1,800 meters would mean tremendous production possibilities. Hybrids developed in the United States generally do not maintain their relative yield advantage over open-pollinated varieties when grown in Mexico. It appears, however, that locally developed hybrids will give yields comparable to those achieved in the United States."

1. These statements are from *Program in the Agricultural Sciences, Annual Report, 1960–61* (New York, the Rockefeller Foundation, July 1961). Also see Arthur T. Mosher, *Technical Cooperation in Latin-American Agriculture* (Chicago, University of Chicago Press, 1957), Ch. 6.

4. In wheat the average Mexican national yield for the 1960–61 season was about 2.5 times the average national yield 10 years ago. After allowing for the favorable climatic conditions of 1960–61, these increases came from more fertilization and improved land preparation and irrigation practices and from the fact that "about 98% of the annual wheat harvest is derived from improved wheat varieties."

"Through the distribution of the new, high yielding varieties Nainari 60, Huamantla Rojo, and Santa Elena . . . it will be possible to increase the average national yields considerably more, and the still newer, semi-commercial dwarf varieties, i.e., Penjamo 62 and Pitic 62, promise to be even better."

5. A new potato program started in 1957 has already developed "nine new blight-resistant potato varieties." "In 1960, over 14,000 tons of certified potato seed were produced in Mexico."

Similar developments are reported for beans and soybeans, horticulture, forage grasses and legumes, and also for "soil fertility and management," "entomology," "plant and animal pathology," and "poultry." The economic aspects appear under "agricultural economics," and there is also a considerable effort to distribute "agricultural information."

By way of an exception, there are a few superior agricultural factors that are ready-made for the purpose under consideration. They are mainly small tools, equipment, and small machines. It is these that private firms are most likely to produce, distribute, and thus make available to farmers in poor agricultural communities.

But most modern agricultural factors suited to a poor community must first be "produced" by starting with established scientific and technical knowledge. The production that this process entails is subject to two fundamental economic attributes. The first is based on the fact that the "producer" in general cannot capture all of the income (benefits) from such production. The second attribute is based on known indivisibilities primarily in the methods and staff of scientists required when a firm undertakes the production of modern factors suited to the agriculture of particular poor communities, starting with the known scientific and technical (agricultural) knowledge.

It is because of these two attributes that it is necessary to "socialize" most basic research and some part of applied or developmental research. If basic research were wholly dependent upon private firms for profit, all too little would be invested in it because such firms cannot capture all of the products of value that a scientific establishment produces.[2] Expenditures of private firms would be less than optimum because marginal costs would not equate marginal returns, since many of the returns are not available to the firm but are widely diffused—some going to other firms and some to consumers. Even though private firms have access to strong patent coverage, they cannot capture all of the returns that flow from research.

The indivisibilities also loom large. A lonely scientist with only a simple laboratory, off by himself in a poor agricultural community, is not likely to accomplish much of anything in starting with the established scientific and technological knowledge to produce new agricultural factors of production technically suited to conditions of the community in which he is situated. So small a scale would be highly inefficient. The methods appropriate to this task as a rule require, to approach an optimum size, a substantial number

2. The first of these two principles is elaborated by Richard R. Nelson, "The Simple Economics of Basic Scientific Research," *Journal of Political Economy*, 67 (June 1959), 297–306.

of competent scientists and assistants and an array of expensive facilities for experimental work.

How close to an optimum is the scientific establishment that has been developed in the United States in meeting the requirements of both of these economic principles pertaining to the production of knowledge useful in agriculture? This establishment consists of state experiment stations, regional laboratories, and The National Research Center at Beltsville, Maryland. The United States Department of Agriculture administers not only the center at Beltsville but also some 200 field installations; the latter are in general too small and too isolated from a scientific community to be efficient.[3] Although the agricultural scientific establishment in the United States has a remarkable record in what it has accomplished, it is nevertheless inefficient on a number of counts. As already implied, it is plagued by too many substations and small federal installations. More important, however, is the fact that a number of major agricultural regions do not have a competent and efficient research establishment serving them. The Kentucky, Tennessee, and West Virginia area, which has a serious low income problem closely related to agriculture and in many ways akin to that in some of the poor agricultural communities throughout the world, has been bypassed. Except for the research establishments in North Carolina and Florida, the South is also poorly provided for. Still another large area not provided for in this respect consists of the plains and intermountain states, starting with the Dakotas, Nebraska, Kan-

3. For a critical examination of the scientific establishment serving agriculture in the United States, see *Science and Agriculture* (President's Science Advisory Committee, Washington, D.C., Jan. 29, 1962), a report on an agricultural panel on which the writer was privileged to serve.

sas, and Oklahoma and extending west, excluding the Pacific fringe served by California and Oregon. The lesson to be drawn from these observations about the bypassed agricultural areas is that it is an expensive undertaking to develop and maintain a large, efficient agricultural research establishment such as exists, for example, in Iowa, Minnesota, Wisconsin, Michigan, New York, and California. The indivisibilities are such that to approach an optimum size many scientists and many expensive research facilities are required.[4] It is worthy of note that the technical assistance programs of the United States in Latin America, although there have been such programs for two decades and although many millions of dollars have been spent on agricultural technical assistance, have not led to the development of a single outstanding agricultural research establishment. By contrast the Rockefeller Foundation, although it has spent very much less on technical assistance to agriculture in Latin America, has succeeded on this score.

The conclusions from this section are as follows: (1) both research and development are, with few exceptions, necessary to adapt known modern agricultural factors to the requirements of poor communities, (2) private firms for profit can as a rule capture only a part of the returns from such research and developmental activities, (3) the size of an efficient research establishment precludes arrangements based on enough firms to assure competition, and (4) the economic basis of (2) and (3) makes it necessary that public and private nonprofit bodies be organized to perform some of these re-

4. For a preliminary treatment of aspects of this problem of producing and distributing new useful knowledge for agriculture, see a paper by this writer, "Agriculture and the Application of Knowledge," *A Look to the Future* (Battle Creek, Mich., Kellogg Foundation, 1956).

search and development functions in supplying modern agricultural factors to communities that do not have access to them.

DISTRIBUTION BY SUPPLIERS

Once new factors of production have been developed that are likely to be profitable in the agricultural economy of a poor community, how are they distributed? Distribution is done predominantly by suppliers who are either profit-making firms or nonprofit agencies.

Yet one observes now and then that the demanders (farmers) have enough information and capacity to perform this function. Subsistence farmers are rarely capable of doing so. Managers of some plantations are able to because of the size of the plantation and because some of them are foreign firms having access to new knowledge abroad. This is closely related to one of the important consequences of colonial economic development which in general did not modernize agriculture except for some plantations. Occasionally there are a few indigenous (commercial) farmers who successfully enter this field of distribution. Some fairly large rice growers in Guatemala, for example, have done so by turning to experiment stations in the rice-growing states—Arkansas, California, Louisiana, and Texas—for information about new discoveries and developments in producing rice. Some of the cotton growers in northern Mexico have done likewise for cotton by turning to nearby experiment stations in the United States.

Firms for profit. The profits that firms can expect to make from distributing new agricultural factors depend mainly upon the costs of entry and the size of the market.

But there is seldom any room for profits from this business in a typical poor agricultural community because costs of entry are generally high and the market for a particular factor is small. Unless the distribution of new factors can be made profitable, it will obviously not attract private firms.

The costs of entry are determined in large part by how much must be spent: (1) on the adaptation of a new agricultural factor to the requirements of the community; (2) on information for farmers who are the potential demanders; and (3) on overcoming other obstacles to entry. The first depends on the extent to which a new agricultural factor has been tried and tested so that it is known to be technically appropriate and profitable for farmers to use. Strictly speaking, these are developmental costs and therefore belong logically under the preceding section. However, in practice a firm that enters a poor community to sell a new agricultural factor will rarely escape some additional developmental costs. It will be convenient to refer to them as "costs of adaptation." They may be small or large depending upon how well the factor is adapted to begin with, how much the firm learns from its local experience, and its efficiency in using such experience to adapt the particular factor to the agricultural requirements of the community. The costs of adaptation are not some fixed proportion of the total costs of the firm because they vary widely from factor to factor and also from one community to another.

The costs to the firm of providing information to farmers about a new factor are a critical variable in determining the role that profit-making firms play in modernizing agriculture. A comparison of the United States and Panajachel, Guatemala, is a useful way of looking at these costs. In the United States there are numerous farm journals, newspapers, radio and television programs that regularly transmit to farm people all manner of technical and economic information. Moreover, the services of these purveyors of information are for hire, and therefore a firm entering upon the distribution of a new agricultural factor can place advertisements and buy time on radio and television to inform farmers about the firm's particular wares. In addition, there is a highly developed agricultural extension service that devotes many of its resources to the task of informing farmers about new factors of production. Yet more important than all of these is the schooling that farm people have acquired. Farm journals and newspapers are obviously not possible when people are illiterate. Complicated scientific and technological instructions about the technical properties of a new factor and its use presuppose a relatively high level of knowledge. Such useful knowledge on the part of farm people is based on their experience and on the level and extent of their schooling.

In contrast, in Panajachel, Guatemala, these complementary firms that specialize in transmitting information to farm people for profit do not exist. Furthermore, there is no agricultural extension service, no relevant technical experience, and no schooling to draw upon. Suppose a supplier offered for sale a better variety of seed that required a specific mixture of commercial fertilizer, a specific insecticide, and a change in irrigation practice; the task of informing farmers in such a community about this new variety and how best to grow it would indeed be a formidable undertaking, measured in terms of costs to the firm, even if the potential market for the new agricultural factor were large. These costs can be critically large.

Private firms are also frequently confronted by political obstacles that entail costs. If it is a foreign firm it may be subject to one or more special conditions upon entering the country. Technical information and breeding stock already established by experimentation pertaining to the new factor may be withheld. For example, in the case of hybrid corn the inbred lines required to produce the crosses for a particular hybrid may not be sold or otherwise made available to firms for profit. Griliches observes that one of the reasons for the relative lateness in the introduction of hybrid corn in the Southeastern region of the United States was the obstacle put in the way of private seed companies in that area in acquiring access to the inbred lines developed by the experiment stations.[5]

Once the costs of entry are determined, what matters is the size of the market. Here the rub is that these markets for new agricultural factors are in general exceedingly small. Mere numbers of farmers do not make a large market. A typical farm in Iowa requires more seed corn than is planted in all of Panajachel! In explaining the differences in the dates at which private seed companies entered the different regions of the United States to sell acceptable varieties of hybrid corn, it is clear that market density was important.[6]

Before private companies can enter this field, it is often necessary for nonprofit agencies to pave the way. As already noted, the cost of entry can be reduced very substantially by nonprofit agencies that disseminate technical and economic information to farmers. Inherent in the costs and returns is a division of labor between firms for profit and nonprofit "firms" in distributing new agricultural factors.

Nonprofit firms. The agricultural ministry of a poor country may undertake a program to distribute new

5. Zvi Griliches, "Hybrid Corn and the Economics of Innovation," *Science, 132* (July 1960), 275–80.

6. Ibid., 276–77.

agricultural factors. Local experiment stations may distribute to farmers new varieties of seeds to be tested under actual farming conditions and to induce farmers to adopt them. An extension service may be established for this and other purposes. Schools may also contribute directly, and very much so indirectly, in the long run by raising the level of schooling of farm people (to be considered mainly in the next chapter). Still others include philanthropic foundations, e.g. the agricultural programs of the Ford Foundation in India and of the Rockefeller Foundation in Latin America; religious groups[7] through the support of schools and agricultural programs; the Food and Agriculture Organization of the U.N.; and foreign governments through programs of economic aid that provide technical assistance to agriculture.[8]

But what can economic analysis contribute to the study of the activities of such public and private nonprofit bodies? The answer lies in the fact that they produce services that have an economic value and to do so they employ resources. While they are not subject to the profit-and-loss accounting of the market, they are nevertheless subject to an economic evaluation, because they incur identifiable costs and produce identifiable returns. In principle the concept of a rate of return is fully as appreciable to investment in schooling, research, development of new factors of production, extension work, and other ways of training farm people through nonmarket arrangements as is the investment in structures, equipment, and inventories that are purchased and sold as

7. James G. Maddox, *Technical Assistance by Religious Agencies in Latin America* (Chicago, University of Chicago Press, 1956).

8. Arthur T. Mosher, *Technical Cooperation in Latin-American Agriculture.*

a matter of course. A basic assumption underlying this study is that it is logically permissible and empirically possible to treat these particular activities of nonprofit agencies in this way. The agencies will be treated as *firms* although they are organized on a nonprofit basis.

Suppose, then, that situations exist where business firms are unable to supply new agricultural factors to poor communities because the costs of entry are too large and the market too small to make it a profitable venture for them. Are there any reasons to suppose that it would be any more "profitable" if one or more of the nonprofit firms were to enter upon this task, once all the real costs that these firms would incur are charged against the returns that would be realized by the community or country from their endeavors? There are indeed compelling reasons for an affirmative answer to this question. For scientific and technological research, they have already been presented. Yet it will be instructive to pursue these somewhat further, because in principle they are also applicable in examining the costs and returns associated with the distribution of new agricultural factors.

The reasons why firms for profit cannot reach a social optimum in undertaking agricultural research are basically of two sorts: (1) they cannot capture all of the returns from the research and (2) they cannot as a rule establish a research establishment of optimum size. Again it will be necessary to turn to hybrid corn to show what this means, because the underlying economics of no other new agricultural factor has been analyzed with such care and thoroughness. The private seed companies, using mainly the inbred lines developed by the experiment stations, did not make inordinate profits. Obviously the experiment stations did not become rich from the successful inbred lines they developed. Yet despite very large research costs, as Griliches shows,[9] the annual return on these research costs was of the order of 700 per cent a year as of 1955. Clearly this extraordinary return did not appear in the income of private seed companies. Nor did it enter the appropriations that supported the experiment stations. Nor did it go to the farmers who adopted the hybrids. It benefited mainly consumers, because it became a consumer surplus by virtue of the fact that it reduced the relative price of corn, which is one of the principal raw materials in producing many animal products. Thus most of the benefits from hybrid corn are to be found in the real income of consumers. If business firms could have captured all or even most of these returns, they obviously would have found it exceedingly profitable to have undertaken all of the research that entered into the development of corn hybrids. But since this is not possible, the only way to produce such cheap sources of additional real income is by developing nonprofit firms of the type under discussion.

The economics of an agricultural extension service is in many ways similar to that of an agricultural research establishment. There are important size considerations. For an agricultural extension service to be efficient, it cannot restrict its activities to the promotion of one or even a few new agricultural factors. It must, for example, also bring to farm people information pertaining to other aspects of production and to consumption and values and tastes that

9. Zvi Griliches, "Research Costs and Social Returns: Hybrid Corn and Related Innovations," *Journal of Political Economy, 66* (1958), 419–31. As of 1955, the cumulated past research expenditure based on a 10 per cent rate of return came to $131 million. The total net annual returns came to $902 million which represents a rate of return of 689 per cent. See Table 2, p. 425.

affect their standard of living. Here, too, it is not possible for a business firm to organize an efficient extension service because of the size of such an establishment and because it could not capture most of the returns. Suppose a country like India were to grant a franchise to a firm for profit to establish a full-fledged agricultural extension service to promote the sale of new agricultural factors; it still would not be a profitable private venture for the reasons already indicated. In the first place, such an enterprise would be exceedingly expensive. In the second place, as in the case of research, it could not capture all of the benefits. Not even all of the gains to be had from additional sales from the promotional work based on providing information to farmers about new agricultural factors could be captured by such a firm for profit unless it were granted a complete monopoly covering all new agricultural factors. It is not conceivable that any enlightened government would grant such a monopoly franchise. Then, too, the business firm could not capture the many other returns that flow from such an agricultural extension service. It might of course be argued that the way out of this dilemma is for the business firm to be given a franchise that not only gives it a monopoly over all new agricultural factors but also the right to charge for each and all of its other services; capturing such other returns would make it profitable and therefore feasible to develop a full-fledged agricultural extension service under the auspices of a profit-making firm. Arguments in favor of this approach obviously require conditions that are so farfetched as to make such an approach wholly unrealistic.

Sight should not be lost, however, of the implications of size conditions in an evaluation of the role that nonprofit firms can play in distributing new agricultural factors in poor communities. It is simply impossible for them to be efficiently organized if they are restricted to a single community no larger than either Panajachel or Senapur.

The practical problem is to find an efficient nonprofit approach for this task. A poor country may induce some foreign agencies to enter, e.g. a foundation[10] or a friendly government or a U.N. agency, to provide some technical assistance. For the most part, however, a poor country must develop its own institutions to perform this function. As this is done, it will pave the way for private companies to enter the distribution of some new agricultural factors. It will then become necessary for the nonprofit firms and the firms for profit to specialize in order to attain an efficient division of labor between them. What is fundamental throughout in supplying these reproducible agricultural factors of production is the prospective high rate of return to investment in the endeavor to modernize the agriculture where farm people are dependent upon relatively unproductive and unprofitable traditional factors of production.

10. Two of the recent annual reports of the Rockefeller Foundation—*Program in the Agricultural Sciences* for 1959–60 (292 pages) and for 1960–61 (326 pages)—are exceedingly instructive on the complexity and scale of foundation endeavor. The financial summary of the expenditures by this foundation on behalf of the agricultural sciences in Mexico, from 1941 through 1960, are reported as follows:

(1) Operating program	$7,317,000
(2) Grants program	1,606,000
(3) Scholarships	292,000
Total	$9,215,000

The annual report for 1960–61 should be required reading for anyone who wants to learn what is involved in developing a successful agricultural research-extension program in a country like Mexico.

11 FARMERS AS DEMANDERS OF NEW FACTORS

According to urban folklore, agriculture is the Gibraltar of traditionalism; hence to think of farmers forsaking custom and demanding new factors of production is absurd. If farmers everywhere were always bound by tradition, it would of course be meaningless to conceive of farmers as demanders of nontraditional factors of production. But modern agriculture is obviously a consequence of farmers having acquired and having learned how to use new, superior factors of production. Nor is this underlying demand for new agricultural factors of production unique, for example, to the renowned farmers of Iowa. Danish farmers achieved such a transformation even before the turn of the century. Farmers in Japan and in Mexico have also been strong during recent decades in their demand for new agricultural factors. The notion that all farmers are handcuffed by tradition, making it impossible for them to modernize agriculture, belongs to the realm of myth.

Farmers as Demanders of New Factors

Having examined the suppliers of agricultural factors, the next step is to consider farmers as demanders of these factors. Three key questions arise. When suppliers make such factors available, under what conditions are farmers in poor communities prepared to accept them? When do they search for such factors even though they are not readily available? How important is on-the-job training, schooling, and experience in learning how best to use new factors? The aim of this chapter is to examine the issues implicit in these questions. The examination entails an analysis of the acceptance of new factors, of the search for them, and of learning how to use them.

RATE OF ACCEPTANCE

What determines whether farmers will accept a new agricultural factor? Suppose that a new factor is available and that the demanders know something about it, including the terms at which it can be acquired. One approach is to explain differences in the rate of acceptance in terms of cultural variables. Another approach, the one pursued here, is to explain the observed differences in the rate of acceptance in terms of profitability.

Profitability. In explaining the diffusion pattern of hybrid corn, Griliches concludes that "one of the major factors accounting for the difference in the rate of acceptance of hybrid corn in different areas was the difference in the *absolute* profitability of the shift over from open pollinated to hybrid varieties."[1] The profitability approach also explains acceptance in poor agricultural communities.

1. See Zvi Griliches, "Congruence versus Profitability: A False Dichotomy," *Rural Sociology*, 25, No. 3 (September 1960), 354. Also his underlying basic study, "Hybrid Corn: An Exploration in the Economics of Technological Change," *Econometrica*, 25 (1957), 501–22.

Despite all that has been written to show that farmers in poor communities are subject to all manner of cultural restraints that make them unresponsive to normal economic incentives in accepting a new agricultural factor, studies of the observed lags in the acceptance of particular new agricultural factors show that these lags are explained satisfactorily by profitability. A pioneering study by Raj Krishna of the supply response of cotton growers in the Punjab, including the acceptance of a new and better variety of cotton, strongly supports this proposition.[2] Tax observes in *Penny Capitalism* that the response to new factors in this community was also active and strong. When seed potatoes, more resistant to blight than the traditional seed, were made available to the Indians in the highlands of Peru, the marked increase in yield that could be realized by using a blight-resistant variety led to a ready acceptance of the new seed. So too in Mexico the experiences are similar with respect to the acceptance by farmers of new varieties of corn and other crops that had a proven capacity to out-yield the traditional varieties.

Since differences in profitability are a strong explanatory variable, it is not necessary to appeal to differences in personality, education, and social environment. The level-of-living indexes actually proved unsuccessful in explaining the difference among states in the rate of acceptance of hybrid corn.[3] Brandner and Strauss took issue in their study of the diffusion of hybrid sorghum in Kansas.[4] But their

2. Raj Krishna, "Farm Supply Response in the Punjab (India-Pakistan): A Case Study of Cotton" (unpublished Ph.D. dissertation, University of Chicago, 1961).

3. Zvi Griliches, "Hybrid Corn and the Economics of Innovations," *Science, 132* (July 1960), 277–79.

4. L. Brander and M. A. Strauss, "Congruence versus Profitability in the Diffusion of Hybrid Sorghum," *Rural Sociology, 24* (1959), 381–83.

issue rests on a false dichotomy between "congruence" and "profitability," as Griliches points out.[5]

The concept of profitability is not restricted to market transactions. Increases in yield of a major subsistence crop, like potatoes in the highlands of Peru and corn in some parts of Mexico, can be "profitable" even if none of the crop is sold. It is likely to be true, however, that the profit possibilities associated with the acceptance of new agricultural factors are in general more restricted for essentially self-sufficient than for commercial farmers. Nor are the effects of the additional production that is sold upon the price of the farm product to be disregarded. When the market is small and the price elasticity of the demand inelastic, the profitability of introducing a new agricultural factor that increases production and sales may shrink over time and even disappear altogether, although farmers are not likely to anticipate this outcome. A large market in which the demand for additional sales by particular farmers is highly elastic with regard to price obviously presents a much more favorable situation. The importance of favorable foreign markets in achieving economic growth in agriculture is often stressed. There have been many such cases. One of the better documented studies on this point is that of Youngson which shows how important the opening up and rapid growth of the United Kingdom market for animal products was for Danish agriculture over the latter part of the nineteenth century.[6] The more recent rapid and large expansion in cotton production in Mexico is not unrelated to the way

5. Zvi Griliches, "Congruence versus Profitability: A False Dichotomy," 354–56.

6. A. J. Youngson, *Possibilities of Economic Progress* (Cambridge, Cambridge University Press, 1959), Ch. 10.

the cotton price supports of the United States maintained a favorable level of cotton prices in world markets, to which Mexican farmers responded most successfully.

Components determining profitability. The mistake made repeatedly by investigators is to take for granted that it would be profitable for farmers in a poor community to acquire and adopt a particular new agricultural factor on no more evidence than that it is profitable for farmers elsewhere to employ this factor. What matters, of course, is the price of the new factor and its yield in the poor community. The price is likely to be relatively high for reasons that will stand repeating, namely that private companies supplying a new variety of seed, fertilizer, insecticide, or a simple machine find the costs of entry high relative to the size of the market.

The components related to yield have not as yet been considered, and they are fairly complex. One aspect that has been mentioned pertains to how successful the suppliers have been in developing and adapting the new factor to the agricultural requirements of the community. Hybrid corn in the United States generally out-yields open-pollinated varieties by about 15 per cent. A poorly adapted hybrid variety available to farmers in a poor community is not likely to be that much better. Suppose, however, the percentage increase in yield were the same, i.e. 15 per cent; to shift from open-pollinated to a hybrid variety in a poor community where corn normally produces 20 bushels per acre will add only 3 bushels to the yield, whereas on an Iowa farm on which 60 bushels an acre has been normal a hybrid variety produces 9 bushels more per acre. In paying the substantially higher price of hybrid seed, it is the *absolute* and not the *relative* increase in yield that matters. To obtain 9 bushels of additional yield, starting with corn that has been yielding only 20 bushels, would require a hybrid that out-yielded the open-pollinated by 45 per cent.

Even though the average annual yield of the new factor is substantially higher than that of the old factor which it replaces, it may vary much more from year to year because of weather, insects, and other pests. Moreover, the true yield variability of the new factor from these sources will not be known, while that of the old factor is well known from experience over many decades. Thus there would be inherent in the prospective yield of the new factors these new elements of risk and uncertainty. They must be taken into account, too, in determining profitability, especially so since farmers in a poor community are less able, in terms of reserves and experience, to cope with such additional risk and uncertainty than are farmers in high income countries.

Farm tenure arrangements can obviously affect the profitability of the new factor to the actual farmer. The way costs and returns are sometimes shared between the land owner and the farmer burdens the farmer with *all* of the additional costs entailed in acquiring and adopting the new factor and gives him only a *part* of the additional yield obtained from it. As is well known, under such tenure arrangements it is not possible for the farmer to equate the extra costs and the extra (total) return attributed to the new factor. When a farmer receives only half of the additional product it implies that the "profitability" that serves as an incentive to the farmer to accept or not to accept a new factor is only half of the true profitability.

To understand the economic basis of the poor results of introducing new agricultural factors in Soviet agriculture during recent decades, it is necessary to apply the approach of farm tenure arrangements just presented. It explains a good deal of what has been happening. The "landlord" in this case is the state, and the "farmers" are the managers of the collective and state farms and the many plot-dwellers who work and reside on the farms and farm a tiny plot on their own.[7] The underlying "tenure arrangements" determine how costs and returns are shared between the "landlord" and the "farmers." The arrangements are such that only a part of the true profitability of a new agricultural factor is to be had by the farmers. Thus the economic incentive to accept, adopt, and use new factors is seriously blunted. Nor has it been possible to introduce most of them successfully from the top.

Thus, by way of summary, as far as one can tell presently the rate of acceptance of a new agricultural factor by farmers in a poor community is best explained by the profitability of adopting and using the factor. The profitability depends upon the price and the yield. Nor will it suffice to examine only the relative increases in yield. The absolute increases in yield are what pay the costs and allow a profit. Differences in year-to-year fluctuations on yield between the new and the old factor that is being replaced can be very important. Tenure arrangements, including the variant developed in the Soviet Union, that determine how landlords and farmers share costs and returns can block the acceptance of factors that would be highly profitable under more appropriate arrangements. Not least, and as yet not considered, is the additional knowledge and skill that may be required to use new agricultural factors effectively. Before turning to these, a brief comment on searching for information is in order.

7. Theodore W. Schultz, "Big Tractors and Many Hoes: A Comment on Soviet Agriculture" (based on observations in the Soviet Union during the summer of 1960), University of Chicago, Paper 6006 (August 1960, mimeo.).

Farmers as Demanders of New Factors

SEARCH FOR NEW FACTORS

Presumably farmers might under some circumstance spend time and money searching for new agricultural factors. There are many instances in the United States where some farmers follow closely the research of one or more experiment stations to see whether any of the new findings would be profitable for them to adopt. A useful analytical way of looking at this kind of behavior of demanders of new agricultural factors is to apply the concepts of costs and returns to the search for information.[8] A reference has already been made to some aspects of this process in preceding chapters. There are, however, no studies on which to draw that have applied this approach to this behavior.

It is highly improbable that any small farmer situated in a typical poor community would engage in such a search unless there were some experimental plots nearby or unless he were to act through some cooperative arrangement. Even if he were of a mind to search for such information, to do it on his own and to extend his search to other farming communities a considerable distance away would become prohibitively expensive for him. To go abroad for this purpose would be out of the question.

However, one would expect that farmers who operate large enterprises would actively search for new agricultural factors. There are many farms in parts of South America that certainly qualify in terms of size, but either the farmers are not very successful in the searching they do or they are inactive in this respect, judging from the obsolete traditional factors they employ. Why they have not done better on this score is a puzzle. The explanation may be that the costs of

8. George J. Stigler, "The Economics of Information," *Journal of Political Economy, 69* (June 1961), 213–25.

adaptation of the new factors have proven to be too high for them.

As noted earlier, managers of plantations appear to engage in this search for new factors of production and to behave as one would predict on the basis of the implied hypothesis underlying the treatment followed here. Yet it must be acknowledged that no careful test has been made. It would be useful to know whether this hypothesis has real explanatory significance. If it does, one could then build on the proposition in pointing the way to enlarging the range and effectiveness of the search for useful information about new agricultural factors.

LEARNING HOW TO USE THEM

It is surprising how little attention has been given by economists, and for that matter by students in other disciplines, to the process of learning how to use new agricultural factors effectively. How much learning is required? Obviously some new factors are simple in this respect while others are exceedingly complex. Hybrid corn is comparatively simple on this score. Yet even here farmers must learn not to select next year's seed from a field produced by a hybrid variety, because it will not reproduce itself as closely as the open-pollinated variety to which they are accustomed—the hybrid soon loses its hybrid vigor where seed is selected in this way. The stalk may be shorter, it may lodge, the ear may be less firmly attached to the stalk after it has ripened, and the kernels may be softer and even different in color. To acquire the best yield, plants need to be planted closer together than is proper with the larger stalk of an open-pollinated variety, more fertilizer needs to be applied, and where there is irrigation the optimum water requirements are likely to differ from those of the open-pollinated variety. So even a simple factor like a corn hybrid entails some learning before the best farm practices can be followed. At the other end of this spectrum, in terms of the complexity of what has to be learned, would be the replacement of common milk cows by a highly productive dairy herd.

It is easy to be misled into thinking that once farmers have successfully substituted modern for traditional agricultural factors, like any once-over change, no or only a little additional learning will be necessary from then on. Surely this is not what is being observed in agriculture in the technically advanced countries. A recent study of a sample of dairy farmers in Pennsylvania tells this story well. They were adopting, between 1942 and 1959, a large array of new agricultural factors. Fliegel and Kivlin identify 43 such farm practices and find that 23 had been adopted by 50 per cent or more of all the farms, and 4 by more than 90 per cent.[9] The large number of new factors of production, the rapid rate of adoption, and, above all, the complex managerial task of fitting all of these together provide a clue to the amount of learning underlying the advance in productivity so characteristic of modern agriculture.

Classification. The learning that is relevant in this connection can be classified into new useful knowledge and new useful skills. They are often highly complementary and in some circumstances the relation between them is virtually fixed, thus implying an indivisibility.

The new knowledge and skills can be acquired in three ways. First there is the time-honored process of learning from

9. Frederick C. Fliegel and Joseph E. Kivlin, *Differences Among Improved Farm Practices as Related to Rates of Adoption,* Bulletin 691 (January 1962), Agricultural Experiment Station, Pennsylvania State University.

trial and error, taught by brute experience. It is often a very expensive way, and technically advanced countries have come to substitute other ways for it because they are cheaper. It is also, in many cases, a very slow way of learning how best to use modern agricultural factors. If poor communities were to depend wholly on this process, the prospects of modernizing in a decade or even over a generation would be bleak indeed. A second way of learning is through on-the-job training. Such training may be provided by firms selling the new agricultural factors, or by a public agency like an agricultural extension service, or by farmers themselves. Training of this kind is done through demonstrations and discussions organized by a private firm or by a public agency. Special short courses and vocational schools are sometimes used. They are as a rule held during the off-season. The renowned Danish folk school was a pioneering success in achieving this aim. Short courses to teach farmers how to operate and take care of tractors, combines, and other complicated machinery aptly illustrate this process. The Soviet Union invested substantially in this approach in its efforts to tractorize field work in producing particular crops. In the United States, the early introduction of the automobile and of gasoline engines for some farm work gave farmers (mainly farm youth) enough knowledge and skill to take tractors and combines in easy strides when they became available and economic. It was literally true that most farm boys already knew all about gasoline engines when farm tractors were introduced. Farmers also learn from each other. The first to try the new is a teacher of his neighbors. Younger persons may work as hired hands for a few years on farms employing modern agricultural factors and thus learn how to use them. Later they become farmers on their own and apply this new knowledge and the new skills. The second way, outlined briefly in this paragraph, is essential where a community is no longer satisfied to wait on the slow results from learning only from experience and wants to do more in the near future than can be achieved through formal schooling. The third, and by all odds the most efficient way in the long run, is schooling. Schooling is here viewed as an investment in human capital; in this case, it is an investment in farm people. The importance of this class of investment in winning economic growth from agriculture in poor communities, taking the long view, is so significant that the next chapter is devoted to it.

Costs and returns. Useful knowledge and useful skills are valuable capabilities that can be acquired for the purpose under consideration through experience, on-the-job training, and schooling. Each of these ways of acquiring capabilities entails some costs and presumably each results in some returns from the additional production related to the new knowledge and skills. The contribution of economic analysis, then, is to examine each of these activities as an investment. Once having determined the underlying costs and the return to each activity, the rate of return on the investment that each entails can be estimated. The differences in the rate of return would then be the indicators to guide private and public investment decisions in this area.

Except for a few recent studies of the economic value of schooling, economists have not examined this area of investment. It has been grossly neglected, even in the United States, despite the large corps of competent agricultural economists. No doubt one major reason for underinvestment in some of these activities, especially in schooling for farm children in the United States, has its roots in the lack of relevant economic information and, as a consequence, a lack of awareness of the extent of the underinvestment.[10]

The conclusions that emerge from this examination of farmers as demanders of modern factors of production are as follows. The profitability of using a new agricultural factor is a strong explanatory variable in analyzing the observed rate of acceptance by farmers. Most farmers in poor agricultural communities are too small and to isolated to undertake a search for new agricultural factors; it simply would cost them too much relative to the return they could realize from the search. Why many of the farmers who own and are responsible for the operation of very large farms, especially in some parts of South America, do not engage successfully in this search for modern agricultural factors is a puzzle. Learning how best to use modern factors entails both new knowledge and new skills on the part of farmers. The knowledge and skills are in essence an investment in farm people. Learning only from experience is not only slow but for many purposes much more expensive than are alternative ways of learning. On-the-job training has a large role to play, especially for a generation, until schooling can take over most of the basic work required in producing the foundation for knowledge and skills.

10. Lee R. Martin's paper, "Research Needed on the Contribution of Human, Social, and Community Capital to Economic Growth," *Journal of Farm Economics, 45* (February 1963) is a useful survey of the literature particularly as it bears on agriculture. See also the author's *The Economic Value of Education* (New York, Columbia University Press, 1963).

12 INVESTING IN FARM PEOPLE

The next proposition has radical social and economic implications. It consists of two theses, namely, that the acquired capabilities of farm people are of primary importance in modernizing agriculture and that these capabilities, like capital goods, are produced means of production. Presumably the level and distribution of the inherited capabilities tend to be the same for large populations. But the acquired capabilities that matter are obviously not given at birth, or at age ten, or at some later age even after secondary and advanced schooling are completed. Although skills and related knowledge can be improved and enhanced throughout life, there are strong cultural and economic reasons for acquiring most of them while young. There is also the basic economic fact that acquired capabilities are not free; they entail real, identifiable costs. They are, in essence, an investment in human capital.

The term "human resources" is being used increasingly to take account of both the quantitative and qualitative attributes of workers whether they are skilled or unskilled, or function as managers, entrepreneurs, planners, and public administrators. This chapter is devoted to the qualitative component of farm people. Investment to increase this component are of several forms; schooling, on-the-job training, and improvements in health rank high. But there are also other ways of investing in farm people, especially in adults who did not have an opportunity to attend school or, if they did, it was all too little to have made them even effectively literate.

The central argument of this study has set the stage for human capital as a major source of economic growth from agriculture. It runs as follows: The economic basis of the slow growth of a penny economy is not to be found generally in observable inefficiencies in the way the traditional agricultural factors of production are allocated; nor is it to be explained by sub-optimum rates of savings and investment in such traditional factors, because the rate of return at the margins is generally too low to warrant additional savings and investment, given anything like normal preferences and motives. The economic basis for rapid growth under these circumstances does not lie in exhortations pertaining to work and thrift. The key to growth is in acquiring and using effectively some modern (nontraditional from the point of view of the experience of people in a penny economy) factors of production. As has been seen, these modern factors are often concealed by economists under an expository contrivance called "technological change." The suppliers of modern agricultural factors are, among others, research people who work in agricultural experiment stations. Their contributions in this connection are of critical importance. Farmers in their role as demanders of the new factors accept them when they are truly profitable. But, typically, farmers in traditional agriculture do not search for them. In the end, much depends on farmers learning how to use modern agricultural factors effectively. At this point, rapid sustained growth rests heavily on particular investments in farm people related to the new skills and new knowledge that farm people must acquire to succeed at the game of growth from agriculture.

But there is the obvious question, does this argument not give too much weight to the quality of human resources in farming? One way to approach this question is to think of farm people comparatively.[1] Suppose the agricultural sector of the United States had exactly the same land and reproducible material capital presently employed in farming, and suppose further that all of the people now farming were replaced by a population whose agricultural experience had been wholly confined to that of farming a century ago and that these people had no schooling. Surely the adverse effects on agricultural production would be very large. To continue these speculations, suppose that by some miracle India, or some other low income country like India, were to acquire as it were overnight a set of natural resources, equipment, and structures and all of the other modern (material) agricultural factors comparable to those employed in agriculture in the United States. What could the farm people of India do with them, given their existing skills and knowledge? Surely the imbalance between material and human capital would be tremendous.

Before turning to the costs and return associated with investment in farm people, there are several preliminary

1. Drawn in part from the author's, "Reflections on Investment in Man," *Journal of Political Economy, Supplement, 70* (October 1962).

issues. These issues may be raised as questions. What about the large increases in agricultural production which have not depended historically on the qualitative component of farm people? What about early industrialization in Western Europe based mainly on an illiterate labor force? Where in agriculture historically has schooling been a source of growth? Why not import the skills that are required?

AGRICULTURAL GROWTH AND HUMAN CAPITAL IN RETROSPECT

Even a little knowledge of economic history raises some doubts about agricultural growth being closely dependent upon the acquired capabilities of farm people. In fact the annals of agriculture show that illiterate farm people have at times increased agricultural production rapidly. Such growth from agriculture did not await schooling and training and better health. These things came afterward, like superior consumption goods, when farm people could afford them. Then, too, in examining the rate of acceptance of new agricultural factors, profitability proved to be exceedingly important over a wide range of cultural differences including differences in schooling and health. Is it not true, therefore, that what is here referred to as an investment in farm people is predominantly consumption?

Several questions need to be faced. What about the economic growth from agriculture by farm people who had little or no schooling? Are there not countries in which the amounts invested in farm people have risen but there have been no discernible favorable effects on agricultural production? Is there not a sharp distinction between industry and agriculture with respect to the level of knowledge and skills required?

The settlement by Europeans and their descendants of

the Americas and Australia and New Zealand led to large increases in agricultural production. Although these farm people were relatively skilled, compared to most other farm people of the world at that time, the key to this era is the opening up of vast territories for a European type of farming, made profitable in large part by the modernization of transportation and the decline in transport costs. (Alfred Marshall in the preface to the eighth edition of the *Principles* makes this development the key in explaining the decline in the rent of land.) This increase in agricultural production was not dependent in general upon farm people acquiring and using effectively a whole set of modern agricultural factors. It called for much brute human force and for some capital goods to farm the new land. The principal explanatory variable was the rapid increase in the supply of farm land. To farm it, the vigor and stamina that go with good health were important. Schooling per se played a small role even in using the several new farm implements that became available for seeding, cultivating, and harvesting some crops. But good farm land is no longer around for the taking, except in a few parts of Latin America and in some areas elsewhere which are still inaccessible from lack of roads and other transport facilities.

The construction of irrigation facilities throughout India, to use another example, also led to much agricultural growth although the water was put to use by illiterate farmers. Farming under irrigation is not a simple matter, but it had long been a traditional way of farming in parts of India. Even so, farmers in the new irrigated areas had much to learn, and the literature is full of laments on how slow and difficult a process it often proved to be.

Nor did the rapid mechanization of field crops in the Soviet Union await better schooling of farm workers. But in this case much was done to supplement the existing skills of farm people. An array of special short courses and training schools for tractor drivers and combine operators were formed.[2] Machinery and tractor stations were established and staffed with persons who had been especially trained to operate and repair the new farm machinery.

In an economy based on slavery, the presumption would be that the owners would invest in having their slaves acquire new skills if it really paid. Since it appears that few if any such investments were made by slave owners in agriculture when slavery existed, the inference would be that it did not pay. But the reasons why it did not pay are fairly obvious. The pay-off period would have been relatively short considering the brief life span of slaves. The work they were required to do (e.g. hoe cotton, cut sugar cane) called largely for brute force.[3] Plantations based on slavery were nowhere

2. Arcadius Kahan, "The Economics of Vocational Training in the U.S.S.R.," *Comparative Education Review, 4* (2) (1960), 75–83.

3. The writer attempted to test the hypothesis that slave owners in the United States prior to the Civil War trained slaves where agriculture required skills and where there were nonfarm skilled jobs that slaves were permitted to do. The underlying facts are hard to come by. But the bits of information that were found supported this hypothesis. For instance, in the large river deltas (e.g. those along the Mississippi River) the demand for slaves was clearly for strong young males to do wholly unskilled brute labor. In the older parts of the South, agriculture had developed a more complex pattern of crops and also some livestock farming, and slaves were also permitted to become masons, carpenters, simple blacksmiths, and butchers who prepared and cured meat. In this area slaves were trained for these jobs. Moreover, slaves with these skills were leased by their owners to those who wanted laborers for this kind of work. In New Orleans, there appears to have been some teaching of slaves to read and write, and a few became sufficiently proficient to serve as tutors. But in other cities where the English language prevailed, state laws prohibited such teaching of slaves. One reason for this prohibition presumably was the belief that knowing how to read and write would enhance the opportunities of slaves to escape to the North. Where French was spoken, this apprehension appears to have been less pronounced.

known for technical progress; they were based on a massive routine in the use of forced labor. Schooling would have been dangerous to the enforcement of this labor routine. But why better health and a longer life span were not realized is baffling.

There is next the issue of investment in farm people associated with little or no favorable effects on agricultural production. It is hard to discern any clear-cut historical cases that support this kind of relationship. There are many examples where better schooling of farm people has paved the way for farm youth to seek nonfarm employment because with their newly acquired abilities they could presumably earn more by transferring out of agriculture. But there are apparently none in which better schooling of farm people who continue at farming is associated with a stagnant agriculture. This then appears to be a false issue.

But there are all manner of historical clues indicating that there has been a strong positive relation between the level of skills and knowledge of farm people and their productivity at farming. One such is the remarkable advance in rice culture and production that occurred just prior to World War I in the United States as a consequence of some Iowa and Illinois farmers moving to lower Louisiana to grow rice mainly as they had previously grown small grains.[4] Another is the comparative success of the farm people of German stock who settled in the Sand Mountain area of Alabama, often cited in this connection. Then too there are many small agricultural enclaves of European and Japanese immigrants in parts of South America who have achieved a higher level of productivity than that of farmers surrounding them.

It is well known that immigrants are often more successful

4. Theodore W. Schultz and C. B. Richey, *Rice Growing in the United States* (Iowa State College, April 1933, mimeo.).

than they were in the country they left and also more successful than the indigenous people in occupations upon which the immigants embark. One hypothesis advanced to explain these dual effects is that people respond to such changes in their economic environment very positively, measured in terms of productivity. An alternative hypothesis, the one pursued here, is of two parts, namely (1) that the relative increase in production in the new situation over that which they left is based on a difference in economic opportunity, and (2) that the relative increase in production that immigrants achieve over the production of their indigenous neighbors rests on a difference in useful skills and knowledge, in which the immigrants in these cases have had a measurable advantage. Although a careful testing of these hypotheses awaits further work, a cursory examination of some records favors the latter.

LESSONS FROM INDUSTRIALIZATION[5]

Since there are strongly held beliefs opposing any substantial investment in human capital during the early stages of industrialization, an examination of these beliefs will further clarify the issues under consideration.

Let us take first the belief pertaining to the order in which things should be done in entering upon industrialization. If a poor country were to spend more of its resources on education, it would have fewer resources to invest in new plants, equipment, and inventories. Therefore, it is argued, there is a kind of natural order in first developing a more productive plant and then, out of the proceeds, spending

5. This section is based partly on a lecture by the author at Southern Methodist University, Dallas, Texas, which appeared in *Foreign Trade and Human Capital,* ed. Paul D. Zook (Dallas, Southern Methodist University Press, 1962), pp. 3–15.

more on education. By following this order a country keeps the horse ahead of the cart. Much history can be cited in support of this sequence. During the early industrialization in Western Europe, plant and equipment came first and school and health facilities followed after a long lag. Governments and the parvenu of business of that period are not famous for their public concern about the welfare of labor. Labor was abundant and cheap; it was mainly illiterate and unskilled; and it did mostly manual work requiring mostly brute force. Incidentally, this capacity to do unskilled manual work is the classical concept of labor to which much of economics is still tied although it is patently wrong. Nevertheless, it is true that programs to improve the skills and knowledge and health of workers were generally not a prerequisite to the advances made during this phase of the Industrial Revolution. Why, then, should schooling be essential today? The answer lies in the fact that poor countries now entering upon industrialization are not employing the simple, primitive machinery and equipment of a century or two ago. Nor could they do so even if they wished to, because such things have become collectors' items for museums.

Another view frequently expressed is based on the belief that a poor country can employ only a handful of skilled people because, as a rule, it is predominantly agricultural, agriculture is backward, and a backward agriculture does not employ highly trained people. Thus, although new skills and knowledge are useful and valuable in high income countries, they are thought to be redundant in poor countries. The issue, of course, is restricted mainly to agriculture, and will be considered later.

A substantial literature claims that there are many "unemployed intellectuals" in poor countries, and this literature goes on to emphasize the social stresses and political dangers inherent in this type of unemployment. Clearly there are some students who, upon their return from their studies abroad, find it hard to obtain work that will put their new skills and knowledge to good use. Education in this context, so it is argued, is a luxury that a poor country can ill afford. The real issue underlying these situations would appear to be whether the skills and knowledge the intellectuals and returning students possess are useful in economic endeavor and appropriate to the economic circumstances of these countries.

Still another belief with regard to schooling goes back to the uses that were made of the large movements of capital from Western countries to less developed countries. This capital was used to build harbors, ports, railroads, textile mills, and some factories and to establish plantations. It was not used to build and operate schools. But it is clear that the capital was, as a rule, highly productive. Are there any reasons why imported capital used for similar purposes today would not give fully as satisfactory results? The central issue here turns on who is to run these new establishments once they have been constructed. In general, as has already been noted, competent European personnel accompanied the earlier capital exports and proceeded to run the new enterprises. This arrangement is now unacceptable to most of the poor nations acquiring capital from abroad. Who then will step in to operate and manage the new port authorities, power installations, railroads, and, above all, the many plants equipped with modern machinery? The lesson to be drawn from recent experiences clearly indicates that *it is sometimes easier to build and construct than it is to develop qualified people to operate and manage such establishments.*

No doubt wherever one turns, a critical factor limiting the economic growth of poor countries is the relative shortage of capital. But this proposition leaves unanswered the questions: What sort of capital? Traditional reproducible forms? No. Nontraditional forms consisting both of material capital and human capital? Yes. The question then becomes whether too much or too little is being invested in material producer goods relative to that being invested in useful skills and knowledge, on the assumption that some education, on-the-job training, and some health services are in essence capital. Recent experiences related to economic aid and to foreign loans to poor countries bear on this question.

Economic aid to poor countries has been much less effective than that to Western European countries after the war. The postwar recovery and subsequent growth of Western Europe has exceeded expectations by a wide margin, whereas the growth of virtually every poor country receiving economic assistance has not come even near to what had been expected. In assessing the implications of the heavy wartime losses in plant and equipment in Europe both from bombing and from wear and tear during the war, economists overrated the retarding effects of the losses on European recovery.[6] The prospects for recovery and growth were *underestimated* because, in identifying and measuring productive capacity, no account was taken of the human capital that had survived the battles and the ravages of the war and the important part that such capital plays in production in a modern economy. On the other hand, the economic growth potentials of poor countries were *overestimated* and for the same basic reason, namely, the omission of human capital as a critical factor in growth; as a consequence, altogether too much was expected from the additions of material capital only, without investment in human capital. The mistaken assessments in both of these instances were a result of relying

6. The author discusses this issue in some detail in "Investment in Human Capital," *American Economic Review, 51* (March 1961), 6–7.

upon a partial rather than an all-inclusive concept of capital.

Another aspect of this issue, which admits of the same resolution, is the apparent low rate at which poor countries can put new foreign capital to good use. The judgment is expressed repeatedly by those who have a responsibility for making such capital available to poor countries that it can be absorbed at best only "slowly and gradually." But this experience is at variance with the widely held impression that these countries are poor fundamentally because they have so little capital and that additional capital is truly the key to their more rapid economic growth. Here again the reconciliation is to be found in shifting from a partial to an all-inclusive concept of capital. The new capital available to poor countries from outside goes as a rule into the formation of equipment and structures. But it is not available for additional investment in man. Consequently, human capabilities do not stay abreast of material capital, and these capabilities become limiting factors in economic growth. It should come as no surprise, therefore, that the absorption rate of capital to augment only particular material resources is necessarily low.

WHERE SCHOOLING COUNTS

Since schooling is the largest and most easily comprehended of the components of human capital, schooling is a convenient proxy of investment in man. When does schooling matter in farming? Increases in yield per acre over time from the adoption, first by producers in one country and then in other countries, of new yield-increasing inputs strongly imply that a widespread adoption of such inputs in the case of sugar cane production has not been dependent upon differences in the schooling of farm people, whereas in the case of growing rice, or of corn, differences in schooling may be a major explanatory factor. In the years prior to World War I, the inequalities in sugar cane yields among the principal producing countries were very large. These inequalities in yields have become much smaller since then. The organization of sugar cane production is based with few exceptions on the mill that grinds and processes the cane. The workers or farmers who cultivate and harvest the cane, whether the mill is a part of a plantation organization or a cooperative venture of the farmers who grow the cane, have been throughout this period largely illiterate. In sharp contrast, rice (also corn) yields have become increasingly more unequal during recent decades. The differences in rice yields correspond closely with the differences in the schooling of rice growers. In countries where the level of this schooling is high, rice yields are also high. The new combination of inputs that accounts for the large increases in rice yields in particular countries, notably in Japan, have not been adopted by rice growers in those countries where the farm people who grow rice are predominantly illiterate.

The adoption and efficient cultivation and harvesting of sugar cane appears not to depend upon the level of schooling of those who do the field work. Nor do the capabilities associated with schooling have any economic value in hoeing cotton. But to grow rice or corn or to undertake dairying, using modern agricultural inputs, appears to be quite another story. This comparison implies a simplified dichotomy based on skills and knowledge on the part of farmers. In one case schooling appears not to count whereas in the other it does.

Growth not dependent on additional schooling. A number of other historical circumstances in which differences in schooling of farm people played only a very small part in agricultural growth have already been examined. They include growth from the opening up of new farm land, from water for irrigation provided mainly by public bodies, and from the mechanization of field crops made possible by skilled mechanics imported from other sectors or recruited from agriculture and trained specially to operate and repair machinery. They also include some growth from the adoption and effective use of new agricultural factors that are profitable when only a few adjustments are required of farmers. It was convenient earlier to refer to hybrid corn as an example of this class. But it too requires new practices to get the best yields. In Punjab, India, the difference in net returns per acre between a hybrid and the local variety of corn was only 10 per cent in favor of the hybrid when local practices were followed.[7] But the difference in net returns per acre rose to 45 per cent in favor of the hybrid when the recommended spacing of plants and application of fertilizer were adopted.

There are still other circumstances in which agricultural growth occurs regardless of the level of schooling. This would be true when new markets for farm products make it profitable to expand production. A recent development of this class already mentioned occurred as a consequence of the cotton price supports by the United States which, during the early post-World War II period, gave cotton-exporting countries a larger part of the world market (and a stable price for cotton). It came at a time when the government of Mexico was completing a number of reservoirs and irrigation facilities in areas very much suited to the growing of cotton. But it would be a mistake to believe that the

7. Russell O. Olson, *Economics of Hybrid Maize Production in Punjab,* Ohio State University Team, U.S. Technical Cooperation Mission to India (December 1958, mimeo.).

prospects are in general bright for the opening up of many new foreign markets for the agricultural products of poor countries. There is much more to be achieved in this connection from investments to improve internal transportation and to provide better marketing facilities, because in many cases such investments would reduce the costs that separate the still all too isolated farmers in poor agricultural communities and the consumers of that part of the production that these farmers sell.

Growth dependent on additional schooling. In general, where technically superior factors of production are a principal source of agricultural growth, schooling counts. This proposition also implies that this source of growth is no longer restricted to the adoption of only a simple new factor, but requires the successful adoption of a complex of such agricultural factors,[8] and, furthermore, the adoption process is a long, continuing one.

The transformation of agriculture in Denmark between 1870 and 1900 could not have been attained without a large investment in the schooling of farm people.[9] The modernization of Danish agriculture is a classic demonstration of the fact that new farm skills and new knowledge about agriculture can be a major source of agricultural growth. A similar agricultural development appears to have occurred in parts of Holland about the same time, although this development has not attracted the attention of students of economic history. The rapid growth of the agricultural sector in Israel[10]

8. Charles E. Kellogg, "Transfers of Basic Skills of Food Production," *Annals of the American Academy of Political and Social Science, 331* (September 1960), 32–38.

9. A. J. Youngson, *Possibilities of Economic Progress* (New York, Cambridge University Press, 1959).

10. A. L. Gaathon, *Capital Stock Employment and Output in Israel,* Special Study No. 1 (Jerusalem, Bank of Israel, 1961).

during the 1950s, especially in dairying and poultry, required a high level of skill and knowledge. The very considerable schooling of the people who entered upon this farming made it possible to acquire these skills and this knowledge rapidly. One could infer from this particular experience that urban people with a high level of schooling have an advantage in modernizing agriculture over farm-reared people with less schooling.

To see the favorable effects of schooling of farm people upon agricultural growth under Asian conditions, the success of Japan is most telling. Despite the severe limitations imposed by the small area of land that is suited for farming, the increases in agricultural production, including increases in labor productivity, have been remarkable. A high level of skill has been achieved in using new knowledge and modern material inputs not only in double cropping but in growing in some areas even three crops a year, and, at the same time, increasing yields of each crop and producing more per farm worker. The modern complex pattern of production activities that characterizes Japanese agriculture has been made possible by two types of public investments: (1) investment in research to discover and develop agricultural factors specifically tailored to the biological and other requirements of Japan, and (2) investment in schooling not only of a corps of specialists to extend this knowledge to farm people but of farm people themselves, which among other things has enhanced their abilities successfully to employ these new inputs which involve complex and difficult farm practices.

As Denmark has done in Europe, Japan has demonstrated in Asia what a country can achieve by applying modern skills and knowledge to agricultural production. As Tang points out, Japan began to invest in rural education "at a time when traditional agriculture could ill justify the outlays even if the government had thought of education as an investment."[11] His study shows that for the period 1880 to 1938 the investment that Japan made in "rural education and research, development, and extension in agriculture" produced a rate of return of 35 per cent per year.[12]

ECONOMICS OF IMPORTING SKILLS[13]

The following question arises in view of the many predominantly public programs to transfer what are thought to be useful skills and knowledge from one country to another by means of technical assistance and related forms of economic aid: to what extent are these programs an efficient means of modernizing agriculture in poor countries?

A low income country can either import particular skills and knowledge or produce them at home. There are in turn two ways of importing: one by inducing foreigners to come and offer their skills; the other by having some people go abroad to acquire a command of such skills and then return. To import skills, a country's firms, persons, and government may employ foreign agronomists, geneticists, soil specialists, economists, and others from abroad who have the skills they are seeking. Some foreign itinerants may be invited to come for a couple of weeks or months, mainly for prestige. (There

11. Anthony M. Tang, "Discussion: U.S. Endeavors to Assist Low-Income Countries Improve Economic Capabilities of Their People," *Journal of Farm Economics* (Proceedings Issue), *43* (5) (December 1961), 1079.

12. Anthony M. Tang, "Research and Education in Japanese Agricultural Development, 1880–1938," *Economic Studies Quarterly* (Riren Keizai-Gaku), (Part I: February 1963; Part II: May 1963).

13. This section follows closely a part of the author's paper, "U.S. Endeavors to Assist Low-Income Countries Improve Economic Capabilities of Their People," *Journal of Farm Economics, 43* (5) (December 1961), 1068–77.

is also a class of light workhorses which can be had for a year or two of service!)

The second way of importing skills and knowledge is to have a select group of people go abroad and master the capabilities. Such individuals may go abroad as distinguished members of a special mission hopping from place to place absorbing who knows what, through ill-prepared and overworked interpreters. Some who go abroad may settle down for a spell either to learn from on-the-job work or from enrolling for instruction and research.

The other source of these skills and knowledge is for the low income country to produce them. There are major shortcomings in what is being done in this respect. Too much stress has been placed on importing and too little on producing the required skills and knowledge within the particular low income countries; too many crash programs and too few enduring enterprises have been undertaken; too much attention has been given to activities at the university level relative to developing elementary and secondary schools; the training and instruction offered to foreign students has been too specific to the demands for skills and knowledge of the economy in which the students study, and thus too remote from the demands for such capabilities of the economy of the low income countries; and, lastly, it has been a mistake to separate the programs for education from programs for economic development.

Import or produce at home. Low income countries differ greatly one from another with respect to the circumstances that bear on this issue. Like the gains to be had from trade, it all depends upon the relative endowments and capacities expressed in the relative prices of factors and products. Nor is it necessarily either one or the other as a rule, for both imported and home-produced skills may be advantageous, each serving different skill requirements. No doubt Mexican nationals working in the United States gain much from the on-the-job training they acquire. Meanwhile, many higher skills can presently be had by Mexicans more cheaply at home than abroad by attending one of Mexico's technological institutes.

The colleges of agriculture in the United States presumably could play a large role in exporting skills and knowledge pertaining to agriculture. Yet only 1,600 of the nearly 50,000 foreign students studying in institutions of higher education in the United States in 1959–60 were studying agriculture.[14] Nor is the number of foreign students studying in the United States large relative to the total enrollment (only about 1.5 per cent compared to six European countries in which between 4 and 30 per cent of the total enrollment is made up of foreign students).[15] What is serious is the relative neglect of developing institutions for this task in low income countries. Unlike some of the foundations, the governmental agencies have had, until very recently, neither the authority nor the capacity to assist low income countries in developing efficient centers for instruction and research.

Crash or enduring programs. One of the principal reasons why government programs have done much less well than those sponsored by foundations is that the government has been committed mainly to crash programs. While there are always some needs that arise unexpectedly and call for a quick, short program, the basic requirements of low in-

14. Kenneth Holland, "Who Is He?" *Annals of the American Academy of Political and Social Science, 335* (May 1961), 10–11, Tables 1 and 2.

15. William J. Platt, *Toward Strategies of Education* (Stanford Research Institute, California, 1961), Table 1. It is of course true that in some colleges and universities in the United States the proportion of students from foreign countries is as large as in Europe.

come countries consist of skills and knowledge that can best be provided by well-conceived, enduring programs of education and research. A few quickly trained mechanics to repair trucks or to overhaul this or that machine, or a small corps of individuals to drive tractors, keep accounts, or operate oil presses, will not fill the bill. Puerto Rico, it might be noted, has done exceedingly well in developing for itself the kinds of schools and institutions that many a low income country requires. Where has public technical assistance had a hand in developing in low income countries the counterpart in this respect of what has emerged in Puerto Rico? They are few indeed.

Distribution among levels of education. There is a profound bias, both on the part of the countries providing economic aid and on the part of leaders in many low income countries, against programs to extend and improve elementary and secondary education. Most of the technical assistance programs have concentrated on public health, agriculture, engineering, industrial productivity, public and business administration, and on some trade schools and vocational training. Grants and aids to students to make it possible for them to study abroad have also favored these areas of specialization. It has been very shortsighted to have neglected elementary and secondary schools. Taking a long-period view, as one must in investing in human capital, the really large pay-offs are likely to be precisely the areas that have been so grossly neglected.

Misplaced specificity in instruction of foreign students.[16] The error here is much discussed but what is done

16. For a comprehensive critical review of the agricultural colleges of the land-grant institutions in this respect, see Arthur T. Mosher, "Discussion: International Opportunities for American Land-Grant Universities," *Journal of Farm Economics* (Proceedings Issue), *43* (5) (December 1961), 1064–67.

to correct it is far from the mark. When students from low income countries enroll in the United States, for example, more often than not they acquire skills and knowledge that are appropriate to the economy of the United States rather than to the circumstances that will confront them when they have returned. Instruction in agricultural colleges would support this inference as strongly as any area of specialization. Most agricultural instruction is short on general principles and long on the specific properties of agriculture of the state or region in which the institution is located. Missions abroad, aware of this shortcoming of so much of college instruction, have countered by requiring some of the students they support to go from institution to institution; but this is worse still, for such rolling stones gather no moss whatsoever. Colleges could and should improve their instruction, for in doing so it also would become much more valuable to American students. The conclusion that emerges, however, is that as soon as possible such instruction should be acquired within the low income country concerned.

Connection between investment in things and people. The logical basis of this connection rests on the concept of an optimum allocation of resources available for investment not only among capital goods but importantly also between such goods and the capabilities of people. Formally, this concept provides a standard for investing so that there will be neither over- nor underinvestment in things or in people. But there are a number of strong biases that make it difficult to attain an optimum.

INVESTING IN HUMAN CAPITAL

While there are some agricultural skills that can be imported more cheaply than they can be produced in a low income country, home-produced skills are always the primary source of the various acquired abilities that are needed for modern agricultural production. To acquire these abilities it is necessary to invest in farm people.

But these investments are burdened with handicaps, and it is not surprising that the amounts invested are as a consequence less than optimum. There is still little awareness that new skills are required in modernizing agriculture and that farming based on modern factors of production is a highly skilled occupation. Some of these handicaps are fundamentally cultural in the sense that manual work, including farm work, is held in low regard in many poor countries. It is then easy to accept the view that anyone who is willing to do manual work and who has a strong back can farm. The supply of whatever agricultural skills are needed is thought to be abundant. In such a cultural setting, it is believed that schooling for farm people would contribute little, for at best it would help improve the national statistics on literacy and perhaps add to the consumption of farm people, which a poor country can ill afford. It is also true that schooling and other investments in farm people as a rule involve both public and private expenditures, and the public expenditures for these purposes are swamped by other conflicting interests.

Political handicaps. There are two major political factors that account for much of the observable *underinvestment* in farm people and one such factor that causes serious *disinvestment* in these forms of human capital. They are as follows: (1) where large landowners are powerful politically, it is to be expected that they will have a strong vested interest in maintaining the status quo; (2) where poor countries are committed to investment in industry as the basic approach in achieving economic growth, agricultural skills and knowledge are neglected; (3) where ideology requires the elimination of private property in land and in other (material) means of production, farm people become strictly farm workers and their entrepreneurial skills are lost.

Clearly the political influence of large landowners is waning throughout the world. The reasons are partly political and partly economic. The democratic process tends to equalize the personal distribution of income and to favor small farmers politically. A communist state obviously destroys large landowners. On the economic side, there are two basic developments. The relative decline of the agricultural sector in a growing economy reduces the influence of agricultural people regardless of the ownership pattern. But more important is the fact that very large farms and absentee ownership are relatively inefficient arrangements for producing animal products, which become a large and increasing part of agriculture as incomes rise with economic growth.

But meanwhile some poor countries are still saddled with politically influential landowners. It should be expected that this group would oppose and delay public expenditures for schooling for the rank and file of farm people. Such schooling in their view could serve no useful purpose and could be harmful. It might become a disturbance weakening their political position. Who knows what might happen politically as a consequence of the routine work of the lowly schoolteacher?

Consider next the widely held beliefs that identify economic growth wholly with industrialization. These beliefs shape economic policy in many poor countries in which governments through planning and developmental programs are endeavoring to increase the rate of economic growth. Typically, one observes the following sequence. Investment begins with industrial plants and equipment. But it soon becomes evident that modern industry requires workers and managers who have modern skills. The omission of investment in such skills is then corrected. Meanwhile, there is the convenient presumption that agricultural production will support the process of industrialization by providing some of the capital required to industrialize, by releasing some workers for the expanding industries, and, above all, by producing enough additional food and other farm products to supply the growing demand at no increase in farm product prices. But then belatedly comes the painful discovery that it is also necessary to modernize agriculture. Once again, the same cycle is repeated, that is, plans are made to provide farm machinery, irrigation facilities, and even more fertilizer. But no plans are made to invest in farm people, and as a consequence they do not acquire the necessary skills and knowledge to use modern agricultural factors effectively.

In countries where ideology dictates that the state must be the landlord and that farm people must be strictly workers, one observes the following sequence. Once such a state has attained sufficient political power, it proceeds to eliminate in principle all private property rights in farm land, farm machinery, and in the other material means of production. In attaining this goal, not only are absentee private landlords and resident farmers who hire some labor dispossessed, but resident, independent farmers (sometimes referred to as peasants or cultivators), who employ their own labor and that of members of their families, are also dispossessed of their property in the agricultural means of production. In taking this step, many agricultural skills are lost, mainly because the economic incentives to apply the skills are destroyed. In extreme cases, large numbers of farmers have been literally liquidated, among them many of the most skilled in agriculture. Thus a serious disinvestment in agricultural skills occurs. Nor has it proven possible under the size and economic incentive arrangements that such a state establishes, in its role as landlord, to adopt and use effectively modern agricultural factors of production. The economic bases of this failure were examined in an earlier chapter.

The three political handicaps that burden investment in farm people are heavy indeed. Although the political influence of large landowners is waning generally, they are still strongly entrenched in some poor countries. The monolithic view that only investment in industry matters in achieving rapid economic growth is gradually being modified and replaced by a more comprehensive view of the sources of growth. Where the state is not only landlord but also lord over all other (material) agricultural factors of production, there are as yet very few signs that the skills and knowledge required for modern agricultural production are likely to be forthcoming.

Classes of investment in farm people. Although for reasons of exposition it has been convenient to concentrate on schooling, there are a number of activities that have the attributes of an investment in man. The following classification is useful in this respect.[17] First, for adults who are committed to farming and who therefore cannot attend regular schools, short courses that come during off-seasons in farming, demonstrations to teach new farm and home skills, and occasional meetings to instruct farm people can

17. This classification is an extension of the one presented by this author in "Investment in Human Capital," *American Economic Review, 51* (March 1961).

play an important role. Suppliers of particular (new) agricultural factors find it profitable under some circumstances to enter upon these activities. Experience has shown that folk schools, community programs, and especially agricultural extension services can be successful in this adult education. Where farm people are literate, published materials and the press generally become a major vehicle of continuing instruction. The radio already serves many poor farm people but television is still too expensive for this purpose except in a few high income countries. Secondly, on-the-job training[18] and apprenticeships, while exceedingly useful in industry, are seldom applicable to agriculture in poor countries. Thirdly, formally organized schools at the elementary, secondary, and higher levels are fundamental in investing in farm people. The underlying costs are higher than is commonly realized because the earnings that students forego while attending school are not seen. The returns from schooling are not to be had in the immediate or even in the near future. The pay-off on schooling is over many years. It is an enduring investment extending into the more distant future. The life expectancy of farm people, therefore, becomes an important variable in determining the rate of return to this class of investment. The costs and return to schooling are examined further below. Fourthly, health facilities and services,[19] broadly conceived to include all expenditures that affect the life expectancy, strength and stamina, and the vigor and vitality of farm people are also a major class

18. Jacob Mincer, "On the Job Training: Costs, Returns and Some Implications," *Journal of Political Economy, Supplement, 70* (October 1962).

19. Selma J. Mushkin, "Health as an Investment," *Journal of Political Economy, Supplement, 70* (October 1962).

among these investments. As has just been suggested under schooling, other things being equal, the rate of return depends upon the expected life span. Advances in health that add five, ten, and more years to the productive life of a people increase very substantially the rate of return on any other investment in human capital. Fifthly, the costs of transferring (migrating) from the job a person holds to a better job can also be treated as an investment in the person making the transfer.[20] Migration within agriculture that is thus motivated is occasionally important. Some farm people left the New England states to go west during the early settlement of the United States. Many farm people have migrated from northeast to southern Brazil. The recent settlement of the "new lands" areas in the Soviet Union is another example. But in general the costs and returns associated with migration that pertains to agriculture are most important in high income countries in which the farm population and the farm labor force is declining.

Economic value of schooling. The costs of schooling, the return to schooling, and schooling as a source of economic growth are receiving an increasing amount of attention by economists. Since what is known is examined by the present writer in *The Economic Value of Education,*[21] this section will be restricted to specific issues pertaining to the schooling of farm people.

Primary schooling is the most profitable of all. It entails the lowest costs per year of schooling when children are still

20. Larry A. Sjaastad, "The Costs and Returns of Human Migration," *Journal of Political Economy, Supplement,* 70 (October 1962).

21. Theodore W. Schultz, *The Economic Value of Education* (New York, Columbia University Press, 1963).

too young to do any appreciable amount of useful farm work. Thus there are only the direct costs, i.e., paying the teachers, covering interest, depreciation, and maintenance of the schoolhouse and paying for books and other current supplies. There are rarely any earnings foregone on the part of children from ages six to ten. Then too, it takes about five years to become effectively literate. The benefits from literacy are many, and some of them are widely diffused. In other words, these benefits accrue in part to the student and his family and in part they are captured by others. Literacy has a pervasive value in reducing costs and in improving the productivity of the economy.

Earlier discussion has already made it clear that the costs of producing and distributing new technical and related economic information to farm people are reduced very substantially when published materials can be used. When farm people are effectively literate, farm journals and the press generally become important vehicles of information. An agricultural extension service can then also use bulletins, pamphlets, and printed instructions which are for many purposes much cheaper than meetings with farmers based wholly on oral presentations.

While the benefits from literacy are many, there are also other economic values from the first five years of schooling. One of these, stressed by Weisbrod, is inherent in the fact that a child who has completed this amount of schooling then has the option of continuing his schooling.[22] The value of more schooling may be large in the sense that the rate of return to the additional investment in schooling is relatively high. Had the student not completed, say, the elementary

22. Burton A. Weisbrod, "Education and the Investment in Human Capital," *Journal of Political Economy, Supplement*, 70 (October 1962).

grades he would not be qualified to enter upon the secondary level, and thus he could not take advantage of the return associated with secondary schooling. Still other benefits from effective literacy are realized when some farm people, usually young people, leave agriculture to take nonfarm employment. Here again, the benefits are of two sorts, i.e., those that accrue to the farm youth as a consequence of his better qualifications and the higher earnings he receives, and those that are captured by others. As Weisbrod shows, in production the employer and the other workers with whom the farm youth works become "employment related beneficiaries," and in satisfying consumer preferences his neighbors become "resident related beneficiaries."[23]

While the economic value of effective literacy is high in an economy where growth is being achieved by modernizing industry and agriculture, literacy is by no means all of the story. Elementary schooling can and should contribute much more, but whether it does depends upon the content of what is taught. Yet what is taught in most poor communities is far from optimum for a society that wants to increase real incomes by modernizing the economy. There are some serious cultural obstacles. The prevailing cultural values as a rule not only exclude the scientific and technological component of modern culture but they debase this important component in what students are taught. Farm people even more than many workers in nonfarm jobs must acquire skills and knowledge drawn from science if they are to be effective in using modern agricultural factors of production. The vocational influence of the parents of farm children on what is taught arises where school administration is decentralized so that the local community has a hand in determining the

23. Ibid.

curriculum. There are many advantages in such a decentralized approach but one disadvantage is that immediately useful or narrowly vocational content is overemphasized. Much of what is learned that is vocationally relevant at the time will be wholly obsolete as agriculture in the community adopts and uses ever more modern agricultural factors.

What is the rate of return to investment in schooling in farm children? For primary schooling, it is likely to be very high except in those communities that continue to depend wholly on traditional agricultural factors and in those that thwart the economic incentives and opportunities to modernize agriculture. These exceptions aside, the rate of return is likely to be high despite the shortcomings of the content of the schooling and the relatively short life span of the people. Moreover, as poor countries enter substantially upon the process of modernizing agriculture, the low level of schooling of farm people soon becomes a limiting factor in the rate of growth from agriculture.[24]

Such clues as are now available all support the tentative judgment that primary schooling is a highly profitable investment. Even though only the benefits that accrue to those who acquire the schooling are taken into account, the rate of return appears to exceed by a wide margin the rate to investment in material capital. Shoup and associates estimate that the incremental return to primary schooling in Venezuela (grades one through six) is 130 per cent per annum based on the differences in the earnings of illiterate agricultural workers and of those who had completed six years of

24. S. Horvat, "The Optimum Rate of Investment," *Economic Journal, 68* (December 1958), 747–67. In his formulation the variable "education and knowledge" becomes a limiting factor of the rate of growth of a poor country.

schooling.[25] In general, estimates of the rate of return to schooling are much higher for elementary than for secondary schooling or for higher education, although the rate for the latter two also exceeds the rate to conventional investments.[26] Within the United States, the rates of return are higher in the South, especially to elementary schooling, than in the North. An incremental investment of 10 per cent to improve and to increase the amount of elementary schooling in the South is likely to yield a 30 per cent rate of return.[27] Studies by Griliches and Gisser show that schooling of farm people is an important explanatory variable of agricultural production and in terms of costs and returns a very profitable investment.[28]

Thus, in sum and substance, the man who is bound by traditional agriculture cannot produce much food no matter how rich the land. Thrift and work are not enough to overcome the niggardliness of this type of agriculture. To produce an abundance of farm products requires that the farmer has access to and has the skill and knowledge to use what science knows about soils, plants, animals, and machines. To

25. Carl S. Shoup et al., *The Fiscal System of Venezuela* (Baltimore, The Johns Hopkins Press, 1959), Ch. 15. A 10 per cent rate is used in accumulating the costs of the six years entering into this primary schooling.

26. Theodore W. Schultz, *The Economic Value of Education,* Pt. III.

27. Theodore W. Schultz, "Education and Economic Goals," *Bureau of Business Research* (University of Georgia, Athens, Georgia), 22 (July 1962); also published by the Agricultural Policy Institute, North Carolina State College. See paper by Burton A. Weisbrod for similar estimates for the South. This paper was also given at the Asheville Conference and is included in the North Carolina State College publication.

28. These studies have been under way at the University of Chicago. Micha Gisser's research is included in his Ph.D. dissertation. These results have not been published as yet.

command farmers to increase production is doomed to failure even though they have access to knowledge. Instead an approach that provides incentives and rewards to farmers is required. The knowledge that makes the transformation possible is a form of capital, which entails investment—investment not only in material inputs in which a part of this knowledge is embedded but importantly also investment in farm people.

INDEX

Index

Index

Index

Index

Index